IMAGINATION
and
Four Other Plays

IMAGINATION

and
FOUR OTHER ONE ACT PLAYS
For Boys and Girls

By
WARREN BECK

ONE-ACT PLAYS IN REPRINT

Core Collection Books, inc.
GREAT NECK, NEW YORK

FIRST PUBLISHED 1925
REPRINTED 1977

Library of Congress Catalog Card Number 77-89720

PRINTED IN THE UNITED STATES OF AMERICA

To
Elizabeth Emily Beck
and
Marjorie Elizabeth Beck

PREFACE

THERE is a real lack of juvenile dramatic literature of a type comparable to the modern juvenile narrative literature. The child has been given an adapted short story and novel, which represent understandably from his point of view the specific human nature of his own kind and age, but this need has not been met so fully in juvenile drama. Few realistic plays about children and for children have been produced.

For children of the early 'teen age plays for acting are especially difficult to select. Fanciful plays abounding in fairies and goblins are frowned upon by the budding adolescent, and yet he finds the drama of mature psychology still far beyond his reach. In the attempt to fill the gap, historical or allegorical scenes and pageants have been given a dominant place, but these have not met the need fully.

The short historical play for children is of necessity episodical rather than dramatic in structure. While the dramatization of historical events may be educationally useful, it is seldom truly dramatic because it must conform to previous general conceptions and to the limitations of the historical facts which the play is designed to carry. A truly dramatic effect is achieved only by abandoning historical proportion and perspective, and allowing human nature to take the center of the stage, and then the character delineation becomes too subtle an art for the child's extremely direct dramatic talents.

PREFACE

Allegorical scenes and pageants are often too diffuse and abstract, so that children perform them mechanically and without real comprehension. Abstraction and generality are foreign to the child's mind. It is futile to try to give the means of vital dramatic expression by encouraging children, clothed in flowing robes, to represent Education, Ambition, Opportunity, Youth and a host of such capitalized anomalies. Such allegory seems arid and unreal to them. They are benumbed by the philosophical weight of it, and they cannot assimilate it.

This lack of purely dramatic literature adapted to the child's mind is more conspicuous in the light of the child's virile dramatic instinct and interest. Boys and girls dramatize much of their recreational activity for themselves, and as they grow older this tendency asserts itself in a desire to act plays. Usually they prefer to represent real characters, and particularly children's parts. But the historical scene or allegorical pageant demand the representation of mature characters, often of a lofty and remote type. The child's attempt to represent characters of which he has no vital concept may be responsible for a part of the artificiality which is sometimes the undesirable by-product of children's participation in dramatics. Instead acting should make the child more childlike, and more himself. This may be accomplished if the dramatic instinct is allowed to express itself in representing the normal child life which the young actors have observed and experienced.

These five plays have been written in an experi-

PREFACE

mental attempt to achieve a more natural type of juvenile dramatic literature. They are the survivors of a number almost three times as large, and their selection has been based upon the test of repeated performances, before some audiences of children and others composed chiefly of adults. The eliminated plays were of various types. Allegory was abandoned after two attempts—quite successful as allegory goes, but no more convincing than Memory, the Christmas Spirit, or Good English ever can be on the stage. One play was rehearsed for two weeks and then allowed to die—of a moral. Several plays were performed and then cast away, because the youthful players never got fully into certain parts that were abnormal or overwrought. Actual testing has always upheld that which was most normally and naturally childlike. The characters in the plays in this volume are all between the ages of nine and fifteen, and the situations are all within the range of the possible experience of American boys and girls.

These plays are not advanced as works possessing great intrinsic literary merit or ethical import but, because of the success of the experimental productions with student casts at Dennis Junior High School, Richmond, Indiana, it is believed that the plays represent real child life with enough truthfulness so that children will perform them with ready insight and natural enjoyment, and that they are so constructed as to lend themselves to a convincing amateur production.

WARREN BECK.

CONTENTS

IMAGINATION

"Imagination" was first produced at Dennis Junior High School, Richmond, Indiana, in May, 1923, with the following cast:

RAY..HAROLD GREEN
BUD..ALVIN REEVES
JIMMIE..MARK GRAFFIS
MARIAN.......RUTH BURDSALL and ESTHER ARMACOST
LOUISE..HELEN HARPER

IMAGINATION

SCENE:—*The living-room of an American city home; the time is in the evening. To the left is a fireplace, with a door beyond it. Before the fireplace is a light settee. Behind this settee, against the rear wall, is a small table bearing a telephone. In the center of the rear wall is a series of French windows, with a window seat under them. At right center is a library table, holding a reading lamp and books and with three chairs drawn up about it.*

(As the curtain rises RAY *and* BUD *are seated at the table reading.* RAY *is a stocky boy of fifteen, whose face is marred by an expression of petulant egotism.* BUD *is fourteen, of a slighter but more sinewy build. His face is lit with chronic good humor.* LOUISE *is curled up on the window seat under an overhanging lamp, absorbed in a book. She is a slender, graceful girl of eleven, full of impish vivacity.* MARIAN *is seated on the settee, reading. Although she is only thirteen, she possesses a really beautiful serenity and womanliness of manner.* JIMMIE *is playing with a puzzle on the floor, center front. His body is small even for its nine years, but his vital spirit burns bright in his eyes and gives him a surprisingly keen and whimsical expression. After the curtain rises there is no sound for a few moments.)*

JIMMIE *(absorbed in his puzzle, half whispering to himself).* Let me see. This goes here and that

IMAGINATION

goes—there—and (*Pauses, in study.*)—oh, yes,— this belongs here, and this here, and —— (*Works feverishly and forgets to talk as he sees the end in view.*) There! (*Leaping up and whooping.*) Whee! I got it, I got it! Whoopee!

RAY (*yelling*). Jimmie! Keep quiet! How can we read in such a row as you're always making?

(MARIAN *looks up annoyed but resumes her reading at once.*)

JIMMIE. But Ray, I got this puzzle worked out —the one Dad bet me a dollar I couldn't do.

RAY. Why broadcast it to the whole world? We're not interested in children's puzzles.

JIMMIE (*turning eagerly*). Marian, you want to see it, don't you?

MARIAN (*absently*). What? Oh, yes, the puzzle. That's good. I'll look at it to-morrow, Jimmie. (*Falls into abstraction over book.*)

JIMMIE (*with profound disgust*). I might have known you wouldn't be interested. All you folks care for is sitting around with your noses in your books. (*Stamping savagely.*) You're a dead crowd!

MARIAN (*looking up patiently*). Now, Jimmie, you're getting tired and cross. It's—9:30. Long past your bedtime.

JIMMIE. I'm not tired, and I'm no crosser than Ray. Why doesn't he go to bed?

RAY (*aroused to defense of his dignity*). Because I'm no child, that's why. I'm fifteen years old. (JIMMIE *whistles in feigned astonishment.*)

[4]

IMAGINATION

And besides, Dad left me in charge of the house and the rest of you.

LOUISE (*sharply*).   I hope one of you wins that debate pretty soon.   How do you think I can read?

(*As argument waxes hot, she holds a pillow to her ear and reads.*)

JIMMIE (*scornfully*).   Are you supposed to be in charge of me?

RAY.   Yes, and I'm telling you now that you must go to bed.

JIMMIE (*turning in appeal to* MARIAN).   Why can't I stay up until Dad and Mother come home? I want to show Dad my puzzle.

MARIAN.   Jimmie, they may not be home from that dinner for an hour, and in the meantime you would surely fall asleep here on the floor.

JIMMIE (*in an inspired and inspiring manner*). Well, then, I'll wait until Bud's father and mother come home, and as soon as Bud leaves then I'll go right to bed ——

MARIAN (*leniently*).   Perhaps you might do that ——

RAY (*coming behind him*).   No you won't. You'll go right now.   Bud's folks won't be back until later, too.

BUD.   They said it would be after ten, Jimmie.

JIMMIE (*meditating a new line of attack*).   Well, then ——

RAY (*barking*).   No, I tell you.   Get along to bed.

JIMMIE (*recognizing defeat*).   Oh, that's where

IMAGINATION

I'm going. You needn't be so grouchy. (*Picks up puzzle deliberately, and carefully places it on telephone table, then turns belligerently.*) If any one of you bookworms smears up my puzzle that took me all evening to do, I'll—I'll beat up on you. (*Crosses stage to door at right front.*)

RAY (*trying to be kind*). Shall I go up-stairs with you, Jimmie?

JIMMIE (*mocking*). No, I'm no infant, I'm nine years old. [*Exits right.*

BUD (*impressed*). He's brave and independent for nine years old, isn't he, Ray?

RAY. That's one thing I'll say for the kid; he's not afraid of the dark. It's nothing to him.

BUD. So it seems. (*Meditatively.*) Well, after all, why should he be afraid of it? He hasn't a vivid imagination. (RAY *looks up.*) That's what makes you afraid of the dark.

RAY. How do you mean that, Bud?

BUD (*with conviction*). It's not what you see; it's what you think you see. It's not what you hear; it's what you think you hear.

RAY (*nodding thoughtfully*). I guess you're right.

BUD. Sure. All Jimmie will see in the dark, and all he'll dream about will be pieces of puzzles. That's nothing to be afraid of. Now, if he had been reading a book like this, his imagination would be full of mysteries and crimes—and it would take the whole family to put him to bed.

RAY. Yes, I see what you mean. (*With stiff dignity.*) Of course, about this reading—we're older—in our case it's different.

[6]

BUD. Oh, yes. (*Turning.*) Louise, can you see a light at my house?

LOUISE (*arousing herself and taking the pillow off her ear*). What did you say, Bud?

BUD. Is there a light at my house?

LOUISE (*peering out window*). No, it's all dark there.

BUD (*yawning*). They ought to be home soon. Said when I saw the lights go on I should come home in a hurry and get some sleep.

RAY. What do you think you'll dream of to-night, after reading that thriller?

BUD. Most anything. Maybe I'll see the villain with the bloody dirk. (*After a pause.*) Ray, what are your sisters reading? Anything hair-raising?

RAY (*with a superior air*). No, I should say not. Probably some terrific story about boarding school life. One of the kind where the terrible climax comes when the girls break the bedtime rule and stay up until eleven o'clock, making fudge in a chafing dish by candle-light.

BUD. There's not much kick to that, is there? Nothing to dream about—unless you ate too much of the fudge. Say, girls. (*Awaits their attention, which they grant grudgingly.*) Why don't you read some real books?

MARIAN. This is what you'd call a real book, Bud.

RAY. What is it?

MARIAN. "Peggy's Last Year at Boarding School." Oh, they have such gay larks.

RAY (*to* BUD). See, what did I tell you?

IMAGINATION

BUD (*scornfully*). Is that the best you can do for a book?

MARIAN (*piqued*). I like it—when people give me a chance to read it.

LOUISE (*coming forward*). Oh, I have the best book of all. It's better than anything you boys ever read. "Mary Martin's Vacation," it's called. She—that's Mary, the heroine of the story—she went to her uncle's in the country to spend summer vacation. They lived in a beautiful big white house, and her aunt gave her some little chickens to raise, and she had a pony to ride and—and (*With elation*) there were some other girls living near and they had a picnic ——

RAY (*breaking in*). There, Bud, that's the grand climax in that yarn. (*Girls struggle between annoyance and aroused interest.*)

BUD (*imitating* LOUISE). How perfectly thrilling! (*In matter-of-fact voice.*) Girls, why don't you get on to some real reading?

LOUISE. What's wrong with this? You couldn't get better stories than the Mary Martin books.

BUD. That stuff may be all right late at night, when you want something soothing to put yourself to sleep, but what you girls ought to read is a real thriller—(*Picking up a book from the table.*) like this one.

MARIAN. What is it?

BUD. "The Mystery of Connault Castle." (RAY *nods knowingly.*) There's a secret passage, and a hidden fortune in jewels, and a mysterious dungeon, and anonymous notes in blood are sent, and people found murdered—oh, it's great!

[8]

IMAGINATION

MARIAN (*dubiously*). It sounds very—pleasant.

LOUISE (*feelingly*). Oh, that must be a horrible book. I couldn't sleep a wink if I read such stuff.

BUD. That's just the beginning. Later on in the story it gets better. A strange man gets into the castle. (*In an animated narrative manner.*) He is apparently acquainted with the secret passage because, while he can never be discovered by day, by night he is heard going from place to place, trying to discover the treasure, tapping on the walls—(*He taps book suddenly to illustrate; the girls and* RAY *start in fright.*) and all who try to intercept him meet with violent death, until there remain only the old earl, who is confined to his bed with gout, the faithful old butler, and the earl's two grandchildren, a little boy and girl who are cousins ——

LOUISE (*hopefully*). I suppose the girl and boy had some happy times, playing around the castle ——?

BUD (*sternly*). Playing? Happy? No one is ever happy in this story; they're always worked up over something—distraught, the books calls it.

(RAY *nods gravely in confirmation.*)

MARIAN (*sarcastic*). It's a very nice book, isn't it, Louise?

(LOUISE *replies with a grimace.*)

BUD (*resuming*). Then, one night at midnight, the little boy is awakened by that hollow tapping on his wall. He sees a gleam of light through a

[9]

crack, then a secret panel slides open, and out steps the mysterious man, carrying a light and a huge club. (BUD *begins to act the part and tiptoes toward the girls.*) He stealthily approaches the bed, with the club raised high and a look of murderous hatred on his evil features. (*Swinging his imaginary club.*) And then ——

(LOUISE *screams and the others are startled.*)

LOUISE (*with fingers in ears*). Oh, stop it, stop it! I'll be afraid to go to bed. (*Walks swiftly to windows, looks out apprehensively.*)

BUD (*disappointed*). I haven't told the best part yet.

MARIAN. Please don't tell us any more, Bud. We don't like it. It's horrible.

RAY. Bud, we must remember that girls can't stand such stories. Those are for men, like you and me. (MARIAN *laughs insinuatingly.*) What are you laughing at?

MARIAN (*sarcastically*). Oh, nothing, nothing.

LOUISE (*looking out window*). Oh, I wish Mother would come home. (*Suddenly.*) There, the lights just went on in your house, Bud. (*Coming forward.*) Now you can go right home.

RAY (*laughing*). She's trying to hurry you along so you won't finish telling that story.

BUD. Sorry I haven't time. I'll finish it when I come again, girls. Good-night. (*With superior grin.*) Pleasant dreams!

[RAY *and* BUD *exit right, laughing.*

MARIAN. Smarties! They make me tired, pretending to be so brave,—I wish they would get a good scare.

(*Door slams, off stage right.*)

LOUISE.   I know I'll dream about that tapping— and the man with the club.   (*Shuddering.*)   Oh!

(RAY *enters right.*)

MARIAN.   Did you lock that front door, Ray?
RAY (*settling down to his book at table*).   Yep.
MARIAN (*musingly*).   I wonder if Mother locked the kitchen door before she left?

(RAY *looks up, showing concern.*)

LOUISE.   Yes, I saw her lock it.

(RAY *turns to his book in relief.*)

MARIAN.   And did Father bolt those pantry windows?

(RAY *shows concern.*)

LOUISE.   I don't know.   (*With fear.*)   I hope so.
RAY (*shifting nervously*).   Say, quit talking about it.   Anyone would think you are scared to death.
LOUISE.   I am, if you want to know it.
RAY.   I don't.   Keep it to yourself.
MARIAN (*suspiciously*).   Ray, you're not afraid, are you?
RAY (*indignantly*).   Of course not.   I'm no silly child.
MARIAN.   Really!
RAY (*on guard*).   What?

MARIAN (*as before*). Oh, nothing, nothing.

(*Silence ensues, they try to resume reading. Then suddenly a very faint squeak is heard off stage left. They all look up, startled and wide-eyed.*)

LOUISE (*in a whisper*). Listen!
RAY (*hoarsely*). What is it? (*Rises, walks toward girls.*)
MARIAN. I thought I heard the kitchen door open.
LOUISE. But I know I saw Mother lock it.
RAY. Are you sure?

(LOUISE *nods, listening intently.*)

MARIAN (*suddenly*). The pantry windows! (*Then with relief.*) Maybe one just blew open. Ray, you might go see.
RAY (*retreating to his chair and making sudden preparations to read*). Oh, no, that isn't necessary.
MARIAN. Is that so?
RAY (*blustering*). Well, what good would that do?
MARIAN (*icily*). Oh, nothing, nothing, of course.
RAY (*muttering to himself*). I wish you would quit saying " Oh, nothing, nothing " as if you didn't mean it.

(*They are scarcely settled in silence again when* LOUISE *suddenly looks up with a startled air.*)

LOUISE (*whispering*). Listen! (*Silence, during which all listen intently.*) Ray, if those windows are unlocked, you could close them.

IMAGINATION

Ray (*awfully*). But if those windows in the pantry have been unlocked all evening, maybe, while we have been sitting here talking, someone has— is —— (*He looks around significantly; the girls seem horrified by the suggestion; simultaneously a tremendous crash of tinware is heard off stage left. The girls scream.*) Burglars!

(Ray *plunges under the table, taking a pillow with him and hiding his face in it.* Louise *disappears in the window seat.* Marian *pulls the light settee forward over herself.*)

Marian (*her head appearing—calling in a tense voice*). Ray!—Oh, Ray.

Ray (*peering out cautiously*). What?

Marian. Dad's revolver is in the table drawer. Can you shoot it?

Ray. Yes—if you'll hand it to me.

Louise (*peeping out the window seat*). Coward!

Ray (*stung, leaping out*). Who's a coward?

Marian. Be quiet. You'll have those burglars in here in a minute. (Ray *rushes under the table again at this suggestion. Urgently.*) Get the revolver. And turn out the lights. We'll have a better chance in the dark.

(Ray *climbs out, gets the revolver, examines it with shaking hands.*)

Louise (*appearing*). Are you sure you know how to shoot it, Ray?

Ray. Yes, Dad showed me how.

Marian. Hurry, Ray, the lights. They may come any minute. (Ray *advances cautiously to left*

[13]

entrance. When he is about half-way there another tremendous crash of tinware is heard in the pantry. RAY *and the girls dive into their respective retreats.* MARIAN, *after they have waited a few moments in silence.*) Ray, put out those lights, or we'll be murdered sure. (RAY *finally emerges, keeps left entrance covered shakily with revolver, crosses stage, turns off room lights by a switch over telephone.*) Put some ashes over the fire too, Ray.

(*He complies, and then as he crawls under the table, he jerks out the table lamp, leaving the room totally dark save for a very faint fire glow.*)

LOUISE. Ray! (*A long pause.*) *Ray!*
RAY. What?
LOUISE. Can you see to shoot?
RAY. I'll be able to as soon as my eyes get used to the dark.
LOUISE. Well, I'm under the window seat; don't shoot me.
MARIAN. Be quiet, Louise.

(*After a moment of silence, a hollow tapping is heard off stage to left.*)

RAY. Listen. What's that? (*Tapping becomes steadier and louder.*)
LOUISE. Oh, these murderers are always tapping on something. (*In a rising wail.*) Oh, daddy, we'll all be killed before you get here.
MARIAN. Shh! We surely will if you don't keep quiet.

(*A flicker of light approaching is seen outside left door.*)

IMAGINATION

Ray (*in horror*). Here they come.

(*The light grows brighter and soon appears to be the circle from a flash-light. The figure behind it comes in the door but remains out of the circle of light, invisible. The light swings about the room, showing it to be apparently empty. The figure, still unseen, moves with its light to the reading table and switches on table light, revealing JIMMIE, attired in a bath robe, eating a doughnut. JIMMIE sits down, eating nonchalantly. MARIAN, peeping out, recognizes him. After she calls his name the others scramble out and, surrounding him from various sides, shout at him at once.*)

MARIAN. Jimmie! What are you doing down here?

RAY. Well, was that you making all that noise?

LOUISE. Oh, Jimmie, you bad boy, how you scared us!

JIMMIE (*startled, leaping forward several steps*). What are you trying to do, scare me out of my growth?

RAY. What are you trying to do, that's what we want to know.

JIMMIE. I got so hungry I couldn't sleep. I began to think of all sorts of things to eat, but especially doughnuts. I knew there were some in the pantry, so I got Dad's flash-light, crept down the back stairs—and got the doughnuts.

MARIAN (*affectionately*). Jimmie, you'll make yourself sick.

JIMMIE (*through a mouth full of doughnut*). Uh,

[15]

uh!—Say, did you hear me knock down those pans? (*Chuckles.*) I got 'em all straightened up, and then I knocked 'em down again.

LOUISE. But what was that tapping noise we heard?

JIMMIE. Tapping? Oh, you must have heard me trying to get that cookie box open. (RAY *shows disgust.*) That thing always sticks when I try to open it quietly.

RAY (*recalling his position of authority*). Girls, let this teach you not to be so silly, and so easily scared. Keep your self-control and be calm, as I did. (*Girls look knowingly at one another.*) Now, Jimmie, what will Dad say if he finds you parading around the house, eating doughnuts? You run along to bed.

JIMMIE. That's where I thought you were. When I made that racket I expected you to come after me, but then when you didn't come I thought you must have gone to bed, especially when I came in here and found—(*Suddenly recalling the situation he had discovered.*) say, why was it dark in here?—Why were you all hiding?

RAY (*vexed*). Look here, Jimmie, you get right along to bed, where you belong, and don't bother us with questions.

JIMMIE (*persistently; turning*). Marian, what was the matter?

MARIAN (*pretending not to see* RAY's *signal to keep quiet*). We heard the noises that you made and thought it was burglars.

JIMMIE (*seeing weapon still in* RAY's *hand*). Is that the reason for the revolver, Ray?

IMAGINATION

RAY (*sullenly*). Of course. It's lucky I didn't shoot you by mistake. Now you get off to bed— and stay there, this time.

JIMMIE. All right, brother. But if any burglars do come, you won't let them spoil my puzzle, will you?

RAY. You talk of puzzles after the danger we've been through.

JIMMIE (*with affected innocence*). What danger?

RAY (*looking aside*). It wasn't exactly danger, (*With fierce directness.*) but we thought it was, and that's just as bad.

MARIAN (*as* JIMMIE *crosses stage to right*). You've been through the danger, Jimmie. You might have been shot.

JIMMIE (*turning at door, right*). Oh, no. You're safe with that revolver, Ray. Yesterday I saw Dad take the shells out of it.

(JIMMIE *exits chuckling;* RAY " *breaks* " *the gun and shows cylinders empty. He and the girls gaze at it in astonishment.*)

RAY. Empty! (*His face brightening with a happy thought*). Well, you'll have to give me credit for that bravery, girls. I faced burglars with an empty gun.

MARIAN (*unimpressed*). But you thought the gun was loaded, didn't you?

RAY (*irritated*). Yes.

LOUISE. And there weren't any burglars to face, were there?

RAY (*savagely*). Oh, be quiet!

(LOUISE *jumps back in alarm.*)

MARIAN (*indignantly*). Why, Ray, you have no right to talk like that to her.

RAY. Louise shouldn't act so smart. If any more burglars come ——

LOUISE (*aroused*). Any more? Any more?

RAY. That's what I said. If any more burglars come, I won't do a thing about it. They may carry off the whole house—and her too—if they want her.

LOUISE. That doesn't worry me. If I want protection, I'll call Jimmie. He's not afraid of— tin pans and cookie boxes. (RAY *snorts and returns to his book, but he cannot settle down. LOUISE wanders to fireplace, reading clock.*) Marian, it's ten o'clock. Won't Daddy and Mother come home soon?

MARIAN. I think so, dear. It won't be much longer now. (*Going to windows to look.*) I don't see them yet, though.—Oh, the sky has cleared. The moonlight is beautiful. Come see it, Louise.

LOUISE (*joining* MARIAN *at windows*). Isn't it pretty?

RAY (*irritably*). You girls stay away from those windows.

LOUISE (*turning aggressively*). Why?

RAY. Do you want to advertise to every prowler on the street that you're alone, watching for your parents to come home? (*The girls are impressed and draw away from the window. In a worried tone.*) There are plenty of burglars out on the streets looking for places like this.

[18]

IMAGINATION

(*The girls return to the settee by the fireplace. Scarcely are they seated when the door-bell rings with sudden insistence.* RAY *looks up with dread on his face.*)

LOUISE (*skipping across stage*). Oh, it's Mother and Daddy come home. I'm going to let them in.

MARIAN (*who has caught* RAY'S *expression of terror*). Stop, Louise. Daddy wouldn't ring; he has his key. Besides, he always whistles to us.

LOUISE (*dampened*). That's right. (*Bell rings.* LOUISE *brightens.*) Maybe it's a caller. Oh, I'm so anxious to see someone.

RAY. Who would be calling at this hour?

LOUISE. Then who is it? (*Bell rings violently.*) I never heard the bell ring that way before. Ray, who is it? Why don't you go to the door?

RAY (*in a voice of terror*). Because I think it is someone who knows we have been left alone and is trying to get in that way. (LOUISE *groans and clings to* MARIAN; *the bell rings again.*) That's what it is, I'm sure. (*Leaping up.*) Better hide again and I'll put off the lights.

(RAY *flashes out the room lights as* LOUISE *is disappearing in the window seat. Just before he turns off the table lamp,* MARIAN *is seen to pull the settee over herself.*)

LOUISE. The ringing has stopped. Maybe he'll go away.

RAY (*under the table*). No, he won't. He knows we're alone and he'll try to get in some other way.

MARIAN. Oh, the pantry windows!

RAY. Look! (*A flash-light plays outside the*

IMAGINATION

windows; a figure in silhouette in the moonlight is seen to pass from right to left. Girls groan.) What did I tell you? That's a real burglar this time.

LOUISE. Oh, Mother, why don't you come home?

MARIAN. Shh. The burglar is coming back. *(The figure with the light returns. Flashes off light and begins hammering gently at the window. The moonlight fades and goes out as if the moon were covered with a cloud. Darkness and the continued tapping on the windows.)* Can you see him, Ray? What's he trying to do?

RAY. I can't see him, the moon's gone under a cloud, but can't you hear what he's trying to do? He's trying to break in that window. *(As the tapping continues occasional groans are heard from the three in hiding. Suddenly the window swings open with a bang, and the flash-light is turned on and sweeps the room. The intruder, unseen behind his light, enters through the window, discovers RAY hiding ostrich fashion, seizes his foot to drag him out, drops his light, and in total darkness a struggle ensues. The girls scream as RAY and the intruder thump about on the floor.)* Help. The burglar has got me. Murder. Help.

THE INTRUDER. Ray. Ray. Don't you know me? It's Bud.

RAY. What? Wait until I turn on a light.

(RAY turns on the table light, revealing BUD sitting on the floor. The boys are disheveled and panting.)

BUD. What were you trying to do, kill me?

IMAGINATION

RAY. What do you mean, breaking into our house like a burglar, and frightening—my sisters?

BUD. You wouldn't let me in the front door when I rang, and I just had to get in. (*Leaping up urgently as he recovers his wits.*) Be still, don't interrupt. There is a burglar in our house. Dad and Mother weren't there at all. This strange man has all the lights on and is going through Dad's desk. I want to call the police.

RAY. All right. Marian, close that window. (*She obeys.*) Here, let me find the number. (*Jerks book from BUD's shaking hands.*) 3-3-1-4. Hurry. (LOUISE *flashes on room lights.*)

BUD (*in 'phone*). Give me 3341—I mean 3314. . . . Yes. Right away, it's burglars. . . . Hello. Police? Say, send a lot of cops down to my house. There's a burglar stealing everything out of my Dad's desk, and my papa and mama are gone, (*Becoming almost breathless with excitement and haste.*) and I'm across the street at Ray's house, and send 'em in a hurry, will you, 'cause he might steal all our stuff —— What? . . . Oh, yes, the house is number 4732 Fremont Street. . . . It's painted gray trimmed in green, and the burglar is in the library—that's the second room off the hall—you just go in the front door like this, and turn this way (*He gesticulates with the telephone.*) . . . What? You can't? (*Bringing the telephone to his mouth and roaring.*) Well, can you hear me now? . . . Number 4732 Fremont Street. Yes, that's right. And say, you better send a —— (*Listens quizzically.*) Hello?—(*To*

[21]

RAY, *as he puts down telephone.*) He's cut off. Oh, boy, now that burglar will get what's coming to him.

RAY.   What's he look like?   Is he as big as your Dad?

BUD.   No, Dad would make two of this guy. He's short and skinny.   I couldn't see his face, just his back.   (*Growing excited.*)   He was going through those desk drawers just as if he were right at home.

LOUISE.   Oh, Bud, how do you suppose he got in? Were any of your windows open?

BUD.   I don't think so.   But these burglars have special tools and they can break in anywhere they want to.

LOUISE.   Then I suppose he'll come here next.

MARIAN.   Don't worry, Louise, the police will come and get him before that.

RAY.   Does your Dad keep any money in his desk?

BUD.   No, I don't think there's anything in that desk except business papers.   I don't know what any burglar would want with those.

(*Outside is heard the roar of an approaching automobile and the clanging of a bell.   Lights flash by outside.*)

LOUISE.   Oh, there's the police patrol.

(RAY *and* BUD *kneel on the window seat and peer out, taking caution to keep the window almost closed.   The girls, standing behind, rise on tiptoe and try to see over the boys' shoulders.*)

IMAGINATION

RAY. There go the cops. Look, Bud, two of 'em are surrounding the house from the back.

BUD. Yes, and those two are going in the front door to get him. Oh, it's locked. Why, they're ringing the door-bell. They must be crazy if they think he'll answer.

RAY. Wait a minute and see. They know what they're doing. Oh, he bit. I'll bet he's surprised.

(*The girls have been trying unsuccessfully to get a peep.*)

MARIAN. What happened, Ray?

RAY. He opened the front door and they grabbed him and took him down to the patrol,—that was pretty easy, huh?

LOUISE (*trying vainly to elbow in*). Let me look a minute.

BUD. Now he's arguing with the cops. Can you beat that? Gets caught in the act and then tries to talk them out of it.—Hah, they won't listen to him. In the patrol wagon he goes. (*The light passes, the bell is heard, and the roar of the motor dies in the distance as* BUD *dances about the stage.*) Off to jail for you, old burglar.

RAY (*vindictively*). I hope they put him in the penitentiary for the rest of his life.

LOUISE (*aghast*). Oh, just think of it. Daddy and Mother gone and this burglar—burglaring all around the neighborhood. Think of us, here all alone.

BUD. Think of me. Think what might have happened if I had bumped into him there in the library.

IMAGINATION

RAY. Did he hear you come into the house?

BUD (*with emphasis*). I didn't go in. I saw that the garage was empty, and I couldn't see Dad's car anywhere, so just for luck I went and looked in the window first.—Then I beat it over here. Say, why didn't you let me in when I rang? I nearly wore my thumb down on that bell.

RAY (*evasively*). Is that so? I didn't hear the bell. It must be out of order.

MARIAN (*to* LOUISE). Something's out of order, believe me.

LOUISE (*to* MARIAN). I'm going to tell Bud that Ray's crooked.

MARIAN (*to* LOUISE). Wait and see what Bud says. I think he knows.

BUD. I'm sorry if I scared you by coming in through the window. But what else was there to do?

RAY. Oh, that's all right. But, you see, we thought it was really a burglar, and—my sisters were terribly frightened.

MARIAN. Of course, Bud, he wasn't a bit afraid.

(BUD *smiles*.)

RAY (*to* MARIAN). You be quiet, I'm telling this. (*To* BUD, *impressively*.) I turned off the lights and laid in wait, planning to attack the intruder at the psychological moment.

BUD (*after catching* MARIAN'S *significant glance, to* RAY). Was that why you had your head muffled up in that cushion?

RAY. What do you mean?

BUD. I was wondering how you could perceive

[24]

the psychological moment with your eyes covered up like an ostrich.

RAY (*stubbornly*). They weren't covered up. I could see everything.

LOUISE (*with spirit*). Bud, don't let him tell you that. He was as afraid as the rest of us. And as for that door-bell, we all heard it, but he wouldn't let me answer it, because he thought it was a burglar trying to get in.

RAY. There you go again. Twice to-night I have risked my life for you, attacking burglars ——

BUD. Twice?

LOUISE (*breaking in*). You didn't attack him, he pulled you out by the foot—like a fishing worm out of a lump of dirt.

MARIAN. And for the second time to-night—it wasn't a burglar, it was a boy.

BUD. Second time?

(RAY *hangs head and sulks.*)

MARIAN. Yes. After you left, Jimmie crept down-stairs and got in the pantry and knocked over a lot of pans. We imagined it was burglars—put out all the lights and watched —— (*With an exhausted sigh.*) Oh, we've had a nice, quiet evening at home, all right.

(RAY *has turned his back in angry shame when* MARIAN *has refused to notice his signals to be quiet about the pan episode.*)

BUD. Well, forget it. It's all over now.

LOUISE. I hope it is. About one more thrill and I'll have to be carried out.

[25]

IMAGINATION

BUD (*patting* RAY's *back*). Come on, Ray, cheer up. Remember what I said to you to-night. It isn't what you have seen and heard, it's what you thought you saw and heard.

RAY. Well, how was I to know?

BUD. You're right. In the dark you can't tell your brother—or me either, from a burglar.

RAY (*with dignity, as one abused*). Of course not.

BUD (*holding him to the point*). But if you hadn't been imagining things, you might have known it was Jimmie in the pantry—and I wouldn't have come in the window looking like a burglar if you hadn't been afraid to let me in the door.

RAY. Oh, you're taking sides against me. (*Turns his back again.*)

BUD. No, I'm just trying to show you what's the matter with you.

(*The telephone rings; all hesitate, looking at* RAY, *who remains with his back obdurately turned.*)

MARIAN (*mockingly*). I didn't hear the bell; it must be out of order. (*Answering the telephone.*) Yes. . . . Oh, yes, Bud is here, Mrs. Keller. (*Aside to* BUD.) It's your mother. (*In telephone.*) Yes, I'll tell him. (*To* BUD.) She wants you to come home right away.

BUD. Ask her if Dad is there.

MARIAN (*in telephone*). Bud wants to know if his father is home. . . . What? . . . Yes, Bud 'phoned from here. . . . Yes. . . . Really? (MARIAN *bursts into laughter; the others*

[26]

regard this conversation in astonishment.) Wasn't that ridiculous? . . . Yes, I'll send him right home. . . . Good-bye. (*Hangs up receiver.*) Your Dad isn't home; he's down at the police station, getting his business partner Mr. Smith out of jail.

BUD. There. I always told Dad that fellow looked crooked, if he was his partner. Dad's foolish to try to get him out. Did Mama say what he was in jail for?

MARIAN (*smiling*). Yes. He was the burglar.

BUD. What? The one I saw?

MARIAN. Your mother said that your father sent Mr. Smith to get some papers from his desk there in the library. You must have seen him while he was looking for them. He tried to explain to the police, but they wouldn't believe him, so he telephoned from the jail to your father to come and get him out.

BUD. What do you know about that?

LOUISE. Bud, don't you know Mr. Smith?

BUD. Yes, I've seen him a hundred times, but ——

LOUISE. Then why didn't you recognize him to-night?

BUD (*ashamed*). He had his back turned, and— I thought he looked like what I always thought a burglar would look like.

RAY (*scornfully*). Imagination!

BUD (*smiling*). That's so! Well, I'm guilty. But notice this, Ray, I admit it.

RAY. You might as well.

BUD (*pointedly*). Some people wouldn't admit

[27]

it.   They might have imagined things and got scared, but they would pretend it wasn't so.

RAY (*after a thoughtful pause*).   I admit it too, Bud. I can see it now. I've been a coward, and a very foolish one at that.

MARIAN.   I'm glad you see it, Ray. We don't blame you for being afraid. We were all as afraid as we could be. It was your imagining yourself a hero that we didn't like.

RAY (*frankly*).   I don't imagine it any longer. I've been scared half to death to-night.

LOUISE.   Me too, Ray.

BUD.   I must go home. Good-night, girls.

LOUISE.   Good-night, Bud.

MARIAN.   Good-night. (*Slyly.*) And pleasant dreams!

BUD (*laughing*).   That makes us even, Marian.

(RAY *and* BUD *exit right to front door.*)

MARIAN.   I suppose Bud won't be keen about seeing Mr. Smith soon.

LOUISE.   Wasn't that funny? No wonder he argued with the policemen when they put him in the patrol.

(JIMMIE *enters right, stops on threshold, uncertain of his welcome.*)

MARIAN.   Jimmie! You up again?

JIMMIE.   Yes. I've been up—for some time.

RAY (*enters behind him*).   Hello, Jimmie. Walking in your sleep?

JIMMIE.   Naw. (*He has a desperate struggle with a yawn and then announces confidently.*)   I'm wide awake.—Say, did you know that the police came and took a burglar out of Bud's house?

LOUISE. How did you know that?

JIMMIE. I saw it out of the window. Did you see it?

MARIAN. Yes, we saw it, out of the window too.

JIMMIE. And did you see that fellow argue with the cops? (*They nod smilingly.*) And they pitched him in and drove off with him and I suppose he's still talking yet. (*With sudden conviction.*) I think I'd like to be a policeman.

MARIAN. Maybe you can be one some day, Jimmie. But why didn't you go to bed after the patrol drove away?

JIMMIE. I did get in bed and got warm, but there's been so much noise in the house that I couldn't sleep—and besides—I want another doughnut.

RAY (*amused*). Sit down by the fire, Jimmie, and I'll get your doughnut for you. (*Goes out left to pantry.*)

JIMMIE. What's the matter with Ray? Is he asleep?

MARIAN. No, Jimmie, he's just waking up.

(*The now familiar, but still tremendous crash of tinware is heard.*)

JIMMIE. You see how it is. You just can't get at those doughnuts without upsetting the tin pans.

RAY (*entering with a plate of doughnuts*). I knocked them over too, Jimmie. (*Passes plate to his sisters, then to* JIMMIE.)

[29]

IMAGINATION

JIMMIE. Yes, we heard you. (*Taking doughnut.*) Thanks, Ray.

RAY (*as he takes doughnut*). Jimmie, I want to see that puzzle of yours. Will you show it to me?

JIMMIE. Sure. (*Brings it to settee.*) You see, this was the hard part, to make it fit here.

(*They all look on.*)

MARIAN. That's fine, Jimmie. I'm afraid I couldn't have done it as quickly as you did.

LOUISE. You're the star of the family, Jimmie.

RAY. That's good work. Anyone who is as good as you are at working out puzzles ought to be a great detective some day.

JIMMIE (*enraptured*) Oh, do you think so?

RAY. Certainly. And you'll win that dollar from Dad, won't you?

JIMMIE (*eating*). Uh. Huh! Believe me, I had to work for it, though. Can't I stay up now and tell Dad about it?

RAY. Yes, I suppose so. It can't be long now.

(JIMMIE *capers about the room in delight, then climbs on window seat and gazes quietly out windows.*)

MARIAN. Will we tell Dad about all the excitement here to-night?

LOUISE. I don't think we had better tell. If they found out how afraid we were, they wouldn't want to leave us again, and then they would never get to go to any more parties.

RAY. No, they needn't feel that way about it,

because there was really nothing to be afraid of. I think we should tell them all about it. (JIMMIE *starts forward.*) And I want to tell Dad that I've worked out a puzzle too. (JIMMIE *shows professional interest at the mention of puzzle.*) I've found out what makes folks afraid of the dark.

JIMMIE. What is it, Ray?

RAY (*smiling ruefully*). Imagination!

(*The curtain falls quickly.*)

THE OLD SLEUTH

"The Old Sleuth" was first produced at Dennis Junior High School, Richmond, Indiana, in May, 1922, with the following cast:

AL	REXFORD HUNTINGTON
CHARLEY	CHESTER COLLINS
BENNY	HERSCHEL CLEVENGER
KATHRYN	CATHERINE FULGHUM
LOUISE	HELEN HARPER
EMILY	ELIZABETH DODD
VIRGINIA	VIVIAN IGELMAN
ELEANOR	RUTH BORTON
DAN	PAUL HARPER
EDDIE	DUDLEY CARTWRIGHT

THE OLD SLEUTH

SCENE:—*A physiology class room in a public school. There are three entrances: one at the rear center opening into a corridor which parallels the rear wall, and two side entrances, left front and right front. At the rear, to the right of the corridor entrance, are two rows of chairs drawn up as for class use. Over these chairs on the rear wall hangs a bulletin board. To the left of the corridor entrance is a bench, or settee, with a solid back. A table, covered with a piece of white oilcloth which reaches half-way to the floor, stands front stage to the right. Several stools are ranged about this table. Against the left wall, just up stage from the front left entrance, stands a large cabinet which is closed.*

(*As the curtain rises,* AL, *a boy of thirteen, seated on one of the stools by the table, is reading aloud from a book; ten-year-old* BENNY, *on another stool, is listening intently.*)

AL (*reading feelingly*). The Old Sleuth paused on the black threshold. The luminous dial of his wrist watch glowed faintly; it was two o'clock. Within this dark house, at this awful hour of night, was to be found the secret of the horrible mystery which for two years he had sought to fathom. To enter now, one man against many criminals, was almost certain death. Yet the Old Sleuth paused only a moment to grip an automatic in each hand and then crept stealthily into that living tomb. All

[35]

was inky black before him. He did not know whether or not the next step would dash him down to death in some horrible abyss. Suddenly, not five yards before him, he heard the faint groans of a human being in agony. Then came a sharp, guttural command in some unrecognizable dialect, a scream as of pain beyond all human endurance, and finally, with a force that seemed to shatter his ears, a tremendous crashing noise ——

(CHARLEY, *age twelve, has entered unobserved at the back, and after listening a moment to ascertain what is being read, he turns indifferently and throws an arm load of books down on the bench with a* crash. AL *and* BENNY *leap into each other's arms with a yell of fright.*)

BENNY. Oh! Oh! What is it?

AL (*stutters in fright*). Why, why,—it's only Charley.

CHARLEY. I hope I didn't scare you. What's the matter?

BENNY. Well, Al was reading about the Old Sleuth, and there came a terrible crash, and we thought that was it.

CHARLEY. What?

BENNY. The Old Sleuth. I mean the crash he heard. It came in just at the right place, didn't it, Al?

AL. Yes, but I ——

CHARLEY (*interrupting*). You must have been badly scared to jump so.

AL (*fully himself now*). I wasn't scared. I jumped up to see who it was. I was going to hide the book if it wasn't you. But I wasn't scared a bit.

BENNY (*credulously*). Not even when the crash came?

AL. Not in the least. When you've read as many Old Sleuth books as I have, you'll have lots of nerve, too.

CHARLEY. How far have you read? Have you got to the place where the Chinaman gives him the drug and buries him alive?

BENNY. Oh, no. Does he really do it? What happens to him? (*He searches frantically in the book with a trembling hand.*)

AL (*snatching book*). Here, you. That's no way to read a detective story. You've got to go through from beginning to end. Take it home with you and read it to-night. I've no more use for it until to-morrow.

BENNY. I don't believe I'll read it to-night. I— I suppose I'll have lessons to study, or something. But I'll take it along. (*He looks at the volume with fond admiration.*) Charley, Old Sleuth was some detective, wasn't he?

CHARLEY. I'll say he was. I'll bet there's not a detective in the world to-day as good as Old Sleuth was.

AL (*seizing an opportunity*). There isn't now, but in a few years there will be.

BENNY. Who will it be, Al?

AL (*hand on chest in a grand manner*). Me! (*His companions stare at him. After stealthily peering out the doors he returns, speaking confidentially.*) I'm going to study being a detective.

My mind's made up. There's a fortune in it for the right person and I know I can do it. I'll read Old Sleuth and scrutinize his methods ——

CHARLEY. What do you mean, scrutinize?

AL. Why, to scrutinize is—(*Impatiently.*)— why,—well, it's what Old Sleuth does, you idiot.

CHARLEY. But he does a lot of different things.

AL. I know, but—well, look here. (*He skims through the book, finds a passage, and reads.*) "The Old Sleuth scrutinized the man carefully. Somewhere he had seen that face before."—There! Now do you see?

CHARLEY. I guess it means to look at. Why don't they say—"Old Sleuth looked at him"?

AL. Look here, Charley, if you can write a better Old Sleuth book than this, you do it. When anyone looks at you, he—he just looks at you; but when a detective like Old Sleuth looks at you, he *scrutinizes* you.

CHARLEY. I see. And are you studying all this so that you can be a detective?

AL. I am.

BENNY. Can you do it now?

AL. What?

BENNY. Detect? Scrutinize? Do like Old Sleuth.

AL. That's what I'm practicing every day. But now I'm beginning to need a couple of assistants, because some of these problems are very complicated.

BENNY. Oh, let me be your assistant. I'll do what you want me to do. I'll obey all your orders and ——

THE OLD SLEUTH

AL (*inspecting him sceptically, just as Old Sleuth might have done*). I don't know about you. You might do. I think I'll give you a chance. You'll have a lot to learn, though, and you'll have to begin at the bottom.

BENNY. That's all right, just give me a chance.

AL. Charley, do you want to join this firm? We'll call it the "Old Sleuth Detective Bureau." I'm the chief, and you could be the secretary.

CHARLEY. That suits me. Let's start to-day.

BENNY. But, if you are chief, and Charley is secretary, what am I?

AL. You? You're—why, you're the force.

BENNY. What do I do?

AL. You do whatever the chief and secretary tell you to do. Mainly your job is to arrest criminals.

BENNY (*aghast*). All by myself?

AL. Certainly. Except in desperate cases. Then I take charge personally, just as Old Sleuth always did. (*He looks cautiously out rear door, then goes to bench.*) Come over here now; let's make our plans for our work.

(CHARLEY *and* BENNY *join him on the bench.*)

BENNY. What do we do to start?

AL. First of all we must find a real case to work on.

CHARLEY. What kind of a case do you want, Al?

AL. I should prefer to start with a nice murder, but if one doesn't turn up we may have to be satisfied with a robbery—jewelry, for instance.

BENNY. I lost a pocket knife last week. Would that be a case?

AL. You lost it? Say, we're looking for criminals, not running a lost and found bureau.

BENNY. The knife's gone. Maybe it's been stolen.

CHARLEY. No one would steal that old pocket knife of yours, Benny.

AL. Besides, what if they did? We want a case with some real crime involved; all the servants found poisoned, for instance, or the man of the house knocked over the head with a poker or an ax handle.

CHARLEY. If that's what you want, it seems to me ——

AL. Sh! Someone approaches.

(KATHRYN, *a girl of fifteen, enters the room right and looks about anxiously.*)

KATHRYN. Have you boys seen a new physiology book? I've lost mine.

BENNY. I haven't seen it, Kathryn.

KATHRYN. I left it here on this table yesterday, and now it's gone.

CHARLEY. Why don't you put up a notice on the bulletin board?

KATHRYN. I think I will. I'm afraid it won't do any good, though. (*She writes a notice and pins it up on bulletin board.*) I've asked everyone about it. That's $2.25 gone for nothing if I don't get it back. [*Exits back right.*

AL (*leaping up*). Aha! Aha! A case.

BENNY. For us? For our detective bureau?

THE OLD SLEUTH

AL. Of course. And a difficult one, too. (AL *studies the bulletin and returns to the center of the stage, where he stands meditating a moment with chin in hand and the best Old Sleuth expression he can muster, while his colleagues look on much impressed.*) After giving the intricate problem thorough consideration, and after a minute examination of all the maze of evidence, I am forced to the inescapable deduction that criminal action is at the bottom of this mystery.—Gentlemen, the book has been stolen.

BENNY (*carried away by* AL's *intensity*). Stolen?

CHARLEY (*remembering his Old Sleuth*). You got that out of Old Sleuth, didn't you?

AL. Got what out of Old Sleuth?

CHARLEY. That speech about ines-escapable deduction.

AL. No. I got that out of my own head. How are you going to be a detective if you stop to ask foolish questions that way?

CHARLEY (*meekly*). I don't know.

AL. Sure you don't. You two don't know anything. Leave it all to me. I'm the brains of this bureau.—Now, let's get to work on this. She's asked everyone; no one knows where the book is, it is not to be found; therefore, it is stolen. Do you follow me?

CHARLEY. Sure, whenever you start.

AL. I mean, do you understand me?—Do you get me?

CHARLEY. Yep. Drive on.

AL. Well, then, the criminal—(AL *seizes* BENNY *by the shoulder in abstract illustration.* BENNY *starts as with a chronic sense of guilt.*) seeing the bulletin, and driven by the poignant pangs of a crying conscience ——

CHARLEY (*with conviction*). That's Old Sleuth, isn't it?

AL. Shut up and listen. The criminal, driven by the poignant pangs of a crying conscience, will endeavor to return the book. Now! We must apprehend him in the act.

BENNY. Appre-apprehend him?

AL. Yes. In order to do that we must maintain watch day and night.

BENNY. Oh, I can't do that. I have to go home at nights.

AL. Then we'll have to begin working during the day, but as the case gets more desperate, we'll have to stay at nights.

CHARLEY. But, Al, the janitors won't let us stay.

AL. They won't know we're here. We'll have to conceal ourselves.

BENNY. Where?

AL (*lifting table cover*). Here, for one place. Benny, get under this table.

BENNY. Now?

AL. Certainly. We must get started on this case. There's not a moment to lose.

BENNY (*after he has crawled under table*). It's awfully cramped under here. Can't I have something to sit on?

AL. How are you ever going to be a detective if you are always wanting something to sit on? Sit on the floor and be still.

THE OLD SLEUTH

CHARLEY. What do you want the secretary to do?

AL. You have to make a report of every word that's spoken in this room, the scene of the crime. You go crawl behind that bench.—Take your tablet and pencil with you.

CHARLEY (*mumbling as he crawls*). But I can't see back here.

AL. What's that you're saying?

CHARLEY (*his head appearing*). I can't see to write back here.

AL. You can't be a detective until you learn to write in the dark, so you might as well begin to learn now.

CHARLEY (*reappearing*). But I can't even hear what's said.

AL. That's another thing you'll have to learn. Listen! I think some girls are coming. Write down what they say, Charley. Benny, if they put their books on that table, you reach up and get them and look for Kathryn's lost physiology book. I'll be in hiding back here. If you are in desperate need, whistle, and yell "Assistance! Police!"

CHARLEY (*arising behind bench*). I'll be in desperate need back here, but it's so dusty dry under this bench that I couldn't whistle.

AL. Shut up. Here's a whistle for you. (*Throws him a referee's whistle on a string.*) Here they come. Duck. (*He hides out back left.*)

(LOUISE *and* EMILY, *two schoolgirls of about twelve, come in arm in arm, speaking with excited rapidity.*)

[43]

THE OLD SLEUTH

LOUISE. I said to her, " I wouldn't think of such
a thing, I wouldn't even consider it under any cir-
cumstances, why what do you take me for," and she
said to me, " Well, I didn't know for sure, but I
thought maybe you would." Now what do you
know about that?

(LOUISE *puts her books at right end of table.*
EMILY *listens to her.*)

CHARLEY (*looking out, writing desperately, whispers hoarsely to* AL *outside*). I broke my pencil.

(AL *peeps in, tosses him a pencil, and waves him
down. The pencil falls from* CHARLEY's *hand, and
rattles on the floor.*)

EMILY (*rapidly*). Oh, what was that? Didn't
you hear that rattling noise? (LOUISE *nods.*) Isn't
this physiology room the spookiest place, with that
awful thing over there in that cabinet? It makes
me feel terribly creepy every time I come in here.

CHARLEY (*looking out and whispering tensely*).
I can't write that down. She goes faster than the
other one.

(AL *looks in and desperately waves* CHARLEY
down.)

LOUISE. I wouldn't study physiology if I didn't
have to, would you?

EMILY (*as she sits at left of table and puts down
her books*). No, I should say not. No one in his
right mind would really want to study such stuff.

LOUISE (*who has wandered back to look at bulletin*). What a shame. Kathryn has lost her new

[44]

physiology book. (EMILY *goes back to bulletin board;* BENNY *looks out, sees his opportunity, and removes* EMILY'S *pile of books, picks out the physiology book, and restores the others.*) The silly things cost two dollars and a quarter. I know, because I was with her yesterday morning when she got hers. I'm using an old one of my brother's.

EMILY. I bought mine this morning. (*The girls return to the table.*) Isn't it frightful waste to pay two twenty-five for a book full of nothing but bones and such stuff? Just look at this—(*She searches the table.*) why, where is my physiology book? I had it here a minute ago. This is yours, isn't it? (*She handles* LOUISE'S *book.*)

LOUISE. Yes, that's my old one.

EMILY (*searching*). But mine is gone. How could that have happened?

LOUISE. Maybe you put it somewhere else.

EMILY. I couldn't have dropped it without noticing, could I?

LOUISE. I don't think so. Did you lay it on a chair anywhere?

(*As the girls search about the room,* BENNY *removes* LOUISE'S *old book.*)

EMILY (*returning to table*). No, I remember putting it right here.

LOUISE (*returning*). Now where's mine? What did you do with it, Emily?

EMILY. I put it back on the table, I know I did.

LOUISE. You didn't; you couldn't have done so or it would be there now. It's with your other books, isn't it?

EMILY. Let's look. But I don't think it's here. (*They search in vain.*)

LOUISE. Well, it's gone for good, I guess. We might as well put up lost notices too. (*The girls write notices.*) These physiology books seem hard to keep.

(*When the girls have gone to the bulletin board to pin up their notices, BENNY nervously returns LOUISE's old book to EMILY's pile of books.*)

EMILY (*at board*). I never have any luck. I'm always losing something.

LOUISE. I've lost three books this term myself. (*As she returns to the table she sees her book.*) Emily! (*She points to the book.*)

EMILY (*returning*). Oh, Louise, it's your book, isn't it?

LOUISE. Of course it's my book. And I don't think you're very nice.

EMILY. Louise, Louise, you don't think I took it, do you?

LOUISE. What else can I think? And I believed you were a friend of mine!

EMILY (*almost in tears*). Oh, I didn't, I didn't. You looked through that pile of books with me just a minute ago. It wasn't there then, was it?

LOUISE. No, that's right, it wasn't.

EMILY. It's this terrible room with its strange noises and that horrible thing. (*She points to cabinet.*) I do believe there's a ghost in here, Louise.

(*At this moment CHARLEY succumbs to the dust behind the bench and sneezes vociferously.*)

THE OLD SLEUTH

LOUISE (*as the girls grasp one another in fear*). Oh, Emily, you are right, there is something wrong in here. I know you didn't take my book.

EMILY. Of course not. And my own is gone and never came back, you remember.

(CHARLEY *sneezes again. Behind the bench it has an uncanny sound.*)

LOUISE. Let's get out of here before anything horrible happens. [*Girls hurry out right.*

(CHARLEY *and* BENNY *emerge warily;* AL *enters frowning.*)

AL (*angrily, to* BENNY). You surely got things mixed up for us. Why didn't you let that old book alone? It's a new one we're looking for. Give me that book of Emily's. (*He snatches it.*)

BENNY (*at* AL's *elbow*). What are you going to do, scrutinize it?

AL (*slamming the book, turning to* CHARLEY). And you, sneezing like a big walrus. How do you ever expect to be a detective if you're going to sneeze at the critical moment?—Let's hear your report.

CHARLEY (*reading*). "Louise: And I said to her, 'Well, I gave the Chink my finger ring, I——'"

BENNY. No, that wasn't it. She said: "I wouldn't think of such a thing."

CHARLEY. Well, that sounds just about the same. Besides, there must be a desperate Chink somewhere in this mystery. There always is.

AL. What else? Read on.

CHARLEY (*reading with emphasis*). "I gave the Chink my finger ring ——"

AL. What else? You read that once, and besides it isn't true anyway. How can you ever be a detective if you can't even copy down what a girl says? (CHARLEY *stares blankly from* AL *to* BENNY.) Go on. Go on.

CHARLEY (*desperately*). "I gave the Chink my finger ring ——"

AL. No! No! That isn't right, I told you. Leave it out. Forget it. Read what comes next.

CHARLEY. But what comes next is a part of this; it's all one sentence, and you must read all of it at once to get the sense.

AL. But you've read that three times.

CHARLEY. Not all of it.

AL. Well, why don't you read all of it? That's what I want to hear.

CHARLEY. How can I read all of it if you keep stopping me?

AL. How can you ever be a detective if you stop to ask questions?

(*There is a long pause during which* AL *glares and* CHARLEY *looks awed.*)

CHARLEY (*timidly*). Shall I go on?

AL. You idiot! (*Folds his arms grandly.*) Continue.

CHARLEY (*loudly, reading*). "I gave the Chink my finger ring "—(*Pauses and looks around triumphantly.* AL *shows annoyance but controls himself.*) "I wanted to get rid of it."

[48]

THE OLD SLEUTH

BENNY. No. No. " I wouldn't even consider it," she said.

CHARLEY (*wearily*). Oh, let him be secretary. I can't hear back there.

AL (*after a pause*). Continue. (CHARLEY *looks helpless.* AL *speaks imperatively.*) Read on!

CHARLEY. That's all.

AL. That's all?

CHARLEY. I couldn't get any more than that written down. I haven't learned to write in the dark, and those girls talked so fast I couldn't hear the words, just a buzz, buzz.

AL. You're a fine lot of detectives, you are. I wish now I'd never taken you into the partnership. I suppose I'll have to go on the job myself now, to save the reputation of the firm.

BENNY. Where will you hide? (*Generously.*) Don't you want my place?

AL. The chief under a table? I guess not. How would it look to have the brains of our detective agency all hunched up under there?

CHARLEY. You may have my place back there if you want it. (*Frankly.*) I don't like it very well.

AL. I don't want it. (*Meditates darkly.*) I know. We'll take old Bony Bill out of his coffin and I'll stand in here.

(AL *opens the cabinet at left stage, revealing a skeleton.*)

CHARLEY. But the teacher will raise the roof if we move Bony Bill.

AL. He won't ever know it. We'll hide Bill and

then put him back. Besides, we must forget everything else in the interests of the case.

(*The sleuths hang back, looking at one another in hesitation.*)

CHARLEY (*stepping forward*). Oh, come on. Grab old Bony Bill; he won't bite us.
(*Cautiously they pull the skeleton out of the case.*)
AL. Don't drop him, whatever you do.
CHARLEY (*in singsong*).

> Take him up tenderly,
> Lift him with care;
> Fashioned so slenderly,
> Young and so fair ——

I learned that in English class yesterday.
AL. Cut out the poetry. Detectives don't go around spouting poetry at the critical moment in a desperate case.
BENNY (*who has abandoned the skeleton to the others and is on the lookout at the rear entrance*). Beat it quick. Here comes a girl.
AL. Oh, where will we put him?

(*They dance about frantically.*)

BENNY. Hurry. Hurry. She's coming down the hall. (*Hides under table.*)
CHARLEY. Here. Flop him on this bench. I'll watch him.

(*They deposit skeleton on bench in lifelike pose; CHARLEY goes behind.*)

AL (*going out left*). What a mess you make of

everything. (VIRGINIA, *a girl of fifteen, enters back right, so deeply absorbed in a book that she sits down next to the skeleton without noticing it. *AL* peeps in at left and whispers hoarsely and pantomimes to *CHARLEY, *who looks out from behind bench.*) Get rid of her. Chase her out. We've got to get that skeleton moved. Scare her out. (*CHARLEY rises cautiously behind bench, loops the skeleton arm over *VIRGINIA'S *shoulders, and ducks. *VIRGINIA *looks up, screams, and runs out right shrieking. *AL* comes in left.*) What a row she made. I suppose they heard her all over the building. Hurry, now, before another girl comes along. Benny, keep a watch.

CHARLEY (*as they pick up skeleton*). I hope that physiology teacher doesn't catch us. He'd crown me for this.

BENNY (*on the lookout at right exit*). Here comes Virginia again, with Eleanor along with her.

CHARLEY. We'll have to skip. Oh, let's put Bill back in his box.

(*They return the skeleton to the case. *BENNY *goes under the table, *CHARLEY *hides behind the bench, *AL* goes out left, and in a moment *VIRGINIA *and *ELEANOR, *a girl of fourteen, come in at right. *VIRGINIA *cowers behind *ELEANOR, *who almost pulls her into the room by her hand.*)

ELEANOR. Where did you see it, Virginia?

VIRGINIA. There it was, right over there on that bench. Oh, Eleanor, I'm still shaking. Just imagine it; it put its arm around me.

THE OLD SLEUTH

ELEANOR. You surely must have imagined it, Virginia.

(*The girls have put their books on the table.*)

VIRGINIA. But I saw it, with my own eyes. I know I saw it.

ELEANOR (*crossing stage*). Here, just to show you that the skeleton is in its cabinet dead as ever, and there's nothing to be afraid of, I'll open the cabinet. (*As* ELEANOR *crosses over to cabinet and* VIRGINIA *follows her a few steps,* BENNY *removes the books, takes out the physiology books, and puts back the others, interchanging the piles in his haste.*) See, Virginia, just a lot of bones. Nothing to be afraid of.

VIRGINIA. It's easy to say there's nothing to be afraid of, but I'm afraid. And I know that—that thing put its arm around me. Please come on, Eleanor, let's get out of this room.

ELEANOR (*returning past table*). All right, Virginia. But calm down, my dear. To-morrow you'll realize it was just your imagination. (*Gathers up* VIRGINIA's *books, looking at them.*) What's happened to my physiology book? Is it with your books?

VIRGINIA. No, I don't think so. (*Looking through* ELEANOR's *books.*) But these aren't mine, they're yours. You must have mine.

ELEANOR (*looking*). I have. (*They exchange.*)

VIRGINIA. And where's my physiology book? It's gone too. I know I had it; and I noticed that you had yours.

THE OLD SLEUTH

ELEANOR. Yes, I'm certain of it. Virginia, how did this happen?

VIRGINIA. Oh, it's this horrible room. Something is wrong in here. The longer I stay the worse I feel. I'm going. [*Dashes out right.*

ELEANOR (*impressed*). Virginia, wait a minute for me. [*Follows out.*

(AL *reënters left;* BENNY *and* CHARLEY *emerge stiffly.*)

BENNY (*handing* AL *books*). Here are some more books for you.

(DAN, *a boy of sixteen, comes to the rear entrance unobserved, is about to enter, when he perceives the unusual manner of the boys and pauses unnoticed on the threshold, listening intently.*)

AL. A fine mess you're getting us into. These aren't what we want. All you do is to grab books off that table.

BENNY. That's all you told me to do.

CHARLEY. At this rate we won't do any good. Instead of finding Kathryn's lost book, we'll have all the other physiology books in our possession, and no way to explain how we got them.

AL. It's all your fault. You fellows have no natural ability as detectives, that's the trouble. Now if I could ever get in that cabinet, I'd soon get some clues that would enable me to solve the mystery.

CHARLEY. Well, come on, then, let's get Bony Bill out of here this time.

(*They open cabinet;* DAN *disappears back right.*)

[53]

BENNY. Where are you going to put him, Al?

AL. We'll put him so far away no one will find him until we get this case settled.

(*They close cabinet and go out back left with skeleton. DAN and EDDIE, a fifteen-year-old boy, enter right cautiously.*)

DAN. All clear now. (*Peers out back.*) There they go down the hall with that skeleton. Oh, this is rich.

EDDIE. Let me in on it. What's up?

DAN. That fool Al is at the bottom of it all. He reads so many detective stories that he thinks he's a sleuth. He has got Benny and Charley to help him, and they're trying to find Kathryn's lost physiology book.

EDDIE. What are they up to now?

DAN. I don't know any more than I told you I heard at the door. Benny sits here under the table and picks off the books. Now Al is going to hide in the cabinet and solve the mystery. (*They laugh.*)

EDDIE. Why can't we break up their little sleuth game?

DAN. I suppose we can. What do you suggest?

EDDIE. Let's put a book here for Benny to take and then when he reaches for it, grab him.

DAN (*laughing*). Fine. But what about Al and the cabinet? Could we upset that?

EDDIE. We might kill the poor boob. Better wait and see what he does first. Listen, here they come. Let's give them a chance to hide.

(*DAN and EDDIE exit right; AL, CHARLEY, and BENNY hurry in back left.*)

THE OLD SLEUTH

AL. On the job, now. Benny, get your hands on everything that anyone puts on the table, but if you can't find the lost book, put back what you have taken. If you do find the lost book, leap out and arrest the criminal, dead or alive. Charley, write down what is said, and make no more bone-head mistakes. I shall be observing all from here.

(AL *enters the cabinet.*)

CHARLEY (*wearily, as he crawls behind bench*). It's a hard life, this being a detective. I believe I'd rather be a burglar.

AL (*looking out from cabinet*). Shut up. You'll have to be a detective because you haven't sense enough to be a burglar.

CHARLEY. "Hark from the tomb what mournful sound."

BENNY. Duck, Charley, here comes a whole flock of girls.

(LOUISE, EMILY, VIRGINIA *and* ELEANOR *enter right. Some put piles of books on the table, close to edge.*)

LOUISE. Show us where you were sitting when it happened, Virginia.

VIRGINIA (*going to bench, others following*). Right here. I didn't notice anything when I came in, and then, all of a sudden, that horrible bony arm was flopping across my neck. Oh, oh,—I feel it yet; I shall never be able to forget it. (*Wipes neck frantically.*)

EMILY. I should have fainted. I know I couldn't

have run; I doubt if I could have screamed even once.

(*In his efforts* BENNY *knocks a pile of books to the floor. The girls, hearing the noise, scream and huddle together near the center of the stage.*)

VIRGINIA. What did I tell you? I knew all the time the place was haunted. Those books simply jumped off that table.

EMILY. I believe you. There must be a ghost in here.

(AL *has been listening with the cabinet door slightly ajar; he allows it to swing a few inches, but does not disclose himself.*)

ELEANOR. Oh, look, look at that door.

(AL *bangs door shut.*)

VIRGINIA. Ghosts. (*Grows faint, clings to* ELEANOR; LOUISE *and* EMILY *start out rear.*)

ELEANOR (*assisting* VIRGINIA *to a chair*). Don't run, girls; we must stay with Virginia, she has fainted. (LOUISE *and* EMILY *return.*) Get me something to fan her with.

(VIRGINIA *revives slightly.*)

LOUISE (*cowering*). This horrible place! No wonder our books are gone; the ghosts steal them. I think it is just a crime to make us study physiology and come to a place like this.

(DAN *and* EDDIE *enter back right.*)

EDDIE. Girls, who has been doing all this screaming in here?

THE OLD SLEUTH

ELEANOR. I guess all of us did.

DAN. What's gone wrong? Virginia, what has made you so pale?

VIRGINIA (*groaning*). Oh.

EMILY. This place is haunted. It's full of ghosts.

EDDIE. Oh, nonsense. That's all your imagination.

ELEANOR. That's what I told Virginia, but I've changed my mind.

DAN. But what has really happened? What have you seen?

VIRGINIA (*weakly*). I saw a live skeleton.

EMILY. It put its arm around her neck, didn't it, Virginia?

LOUISE. And our books have been disappearing. We put them down on this table, and the next moment they are gone.

EMILY. The ghosts take them.

DAN. You must be mistaken. That couldn't be possible.

LOUISE. It may be impossible, but it's been happening all morning.

DAN (*loudly*). There's Kathryn's physiology book on the table; they haven't taken that. (*The table is really empty, but* BENNY *forgets himself and reaches out frantically;* EDDIE *seizes him by the wrist and drags him out. Girls scream.*) There's your ghost.

BENNY (*after looking in disappointment at empty table*). I'm not a ghost. I'm a ——

LOUISE. Oh, you young villain. So you've been doing all this.

THE OLD SLEUTH

EMILY. Where's my book? What did you do with it?

ELEANOR. And where's mine, you young thief?

BENNY. But I'm not a thief, I'm a detective ——

(*They laugh at him.*)

EDDIE. No, you're wrong again; you're not a detective, you're a joke. (AL *has allowed the cabinet door to swing partially open and is watching open-mouthed.*) Here's your mystery, girls.

VIRGINIA. But this still doesn't explain the live skeleton that put its arm around me.

(AL *suddenly bangs door in fright.*)

DAN (*in loud pretense*). Listen. Did you hear that door? There may be a ghost in there after all. Eddie, get me nails and a hammer. If there's a ghost in here I'll nail it up.

(AL *shrieks from inside, girls show horror,* DAN *pantomimes nailing door.*)

EDDIE. We've caught a ghost, surely. I wonder how we can kill it.

AL (*inside*). Let me out. Let me out.

DAN (*solemnly, shouting at crack so* AL *can hear*). What we had best do to drive away the ghost is to build a big fire and throw the cabinet and all on without even opening it.

AL (*frantically*). Help. Help. Don't burn me.

VIRGINIA. Oh, this is terrible.

EMILY. I've never been so scared in all my life.

EDDIE. Don't worry, girls, that's no ghost, just another detective.

[58]

THE OLD SLEUTH

DAN (*addressing box*). If I let you out, will you be a good ghost?

AL. I'll do anything to get out.

DAN. And you'll promise not to hurt any of us?

AL. No. No. Let me out, I'm smothered.

DAN. All right, terrible ghost, step forth.

(*Girls retreat to right stage,* DAN *opens door,* AL *collapses to floor.*)

LOUISE. Al! Where's the skeleton?

EMILY. What was he doing in there?

DAN. He's another of the amateur detectives trying to find Kathryn's lost physiology book.

ELEANOR. Did Kathryn hire them to look for it?

DAN. I don't know. Did she, Old Sleuth?

(AL *shakes head miserably.* KATHRYN *enters right.*)

ELEANOR. Oh, Kathryn, have you found your lost book?

KATHRYN. It isn't lost, after all. I found it under some paper in the bottom of my locker.

(AL *and* BENNY *look disgusted, the others laugh,* KATHRYN *goes to bulletin board and tears down her notice.*)

EDDIE. Well, it's caused enough trouble as it is.

KATHRYN. How is that? Have you all been spending the day looking for it?

EDDIE. These fellows have. They read your notice and formed a detective agency to recover your book.

KATHRYN. You seem to be taking them very

seriously. Why not let the little boys go on with their game?

(AL *writhes.*)

DAN. Kathryn, they've been stealing other folks' books trying to find yours.

LOUISE. Yes, and they've frightened us all nearly to death.

KATHRYN. I'm sorry for that. They don't look so frightful now, do they? (*All laugh at the detectives' discomfiture.*) But is this the entire force? I saw Charley in here with these two. Maybe he's in on it.

DAN. Sure he is. I forgot all about him. Where is he, Old Sleuth? (*Shakes* AL *by arm, but* AL *remains silent with a martyr's obduracy.*)

EDDIE (*shaking* BENNIE). Where is Charley? You might as well tell us now. Where is he?

BENNY (*sullenly*). Back of the bench.

DAN. Go get him, Eddie. Girls, hold Benny.

(EDDIE *hands over his captive to two of the girls, creeps back, looks over bench, laughs in surprise, holds up finger for silence, pulls bench aside and reveals* CHARLEY *in sound slumber.*)

EDDIE (*whispering*). Let's scare him. One—two—three—booh? (*Others nod assent.*) One—two—three ——

ALL (*explosively*). *Booh!*

CHARLEY (*leaping up and blowing desperately on his whistle*). Assistance! Police! Help! (*Starts across stage to right.* EDDIE *seizes him.*)

EDDIE. You might as well surrender; the rest of the force is captured.

THE OLD SLEUTH

AL (*bitterly*). You're a fine detective! Going to sleep on the job! How do you expect to be a detective if you can't keep awake?

BENNY (*with sudden spirit*). Be quiet, Al. You don't know anything yourself about being a detective. I resign from your force.

CHARLEY. Yes, I quit too. Get a new secretary. I'm through.

DAN (*in a grand manner*). Ladies and gentlemen, how shall we reward these great detectives who have so devotedly given their skilled services and have so heroically braved terrible dangers and suffered awful hardships to solve the baffling mystery of the lost physiology book?

CHARLEY (*wearily*). That's some more out of Old Sleuth. I've heard enough of that.

EDDIE (*continuing DAN's burlesque*). I have read somewhere that fame is the detective's greatest reward. Let the glorious fame with which these detectives have covered themselves be their chief recompense. (*Others laugh and applaud.*)

CHARLEY. Oh, don't rub it in. I feel like a fool as it is.

DAN (*stroking AL's arm as he holds him captive*). This feels like a fool, too.

AL (*jerking away*). Oh, how do you expect ——

CHARLEY (*interrupting*). Bah! We don't expect anything from you ——

BENNY. Except going on acting the fool.

DAN (*shaking him*). Wake up, Al. It's morning. Your dream is over.

AL (*his pride broken*). Oh, I know I'm a boob.

[61]

THE OLD SLEUTH

BENNY. You're only the last one in the crowd to find it out; that's not so bad for you.

VIRGINIA. But there's still a mystery here. All this playing detective doesn't explain the skeleton. I am positive I saw it. It was a live skeleton, I know.

EDDIE. What about it, sleuths? Can you solve this mystery?

CHARLEY. That was old Bony Bill you saw. We had it there on the bench when you sat down, but you were so busy with your book that you didn't notice it. (*He hesitates.*)

VIRGINIA. But old Bony Bill couldn't put its arm around me and I know this one did.

CHARLEY. I looped its arm around you to get you out of the room.

VIRGINIA (*suddenly incensed*). Oh, you nasty wretch.

(VIRGINIA *chases* CHARLEY *out right, others follow laughing and shouting encouragement in the chase. The tumult echoes and dies down a hall. BENNY and AL have been deserted on the stage. They survey one another with mutual disgust; BENNY shrugs his shoulders and goes out back. AL, seeing the fatal volume of Old Sleuth on the floor, picks it up, stares at it intently a moment, then in a sudden rage he dashes it on the floor and shambles disconsolately out the left. The curtain falls.*)

GREAT CÆSAR

"Great Cæsar" was first produced at Dennis Junior High School, Richmond, Indiana, in May, 1923, with the following cast:

HARRY	DUDLEY CARTWRIGHT
JOE	ROBERT SURENDORF
BILLY	FLOYD GARDNER
GEORGE	CHESTER COLLINS
JANE	FRANCES MAHAN
LUCILLE	MARIE MACKEY
SAM	FRANCIS PEACOCK

GREAT CÆSAR

SCENE:—*Is in a roomy barn loft with four entrances: front and back stage both right and left. A large window at the back is open and reveals a country village scene of cottage roof-tops and flourishing gardens. The small amount of hay which the loft contains has been raked to the side walls. Barrels, boxes, and boards clutter up the floor.*

(As the curtain rises the four boys who occupy the loft are making signs announcing an amateur dramatic-enactment.

JOE, *age twelve, is a chubby, freckled boy; barefooted and clad in overalls. His numerous freckles veil the vacancy of his face.*

HARRY, *age thirteen, is slender and wiry. He is dressed in a shirt and pants whacked off in an approximate fit which strikes him half-way between knee and ankle. HARRY delights in hitching his thumbs in a broad pair of suspenders, which look as though they might have been inherited with the pants. He wears shoes, but no stockings. His thin face is virile and eagerly alert.*

BILLY, *age ten, is physically small and is neatly dressed. His eyes, disconcertingly direct, reveal him as precocious in the ways of his world.*

GEORGE, *age fifteen, is huge in bulk but animation is absent from his make-up. He is dressed in a torn shirt, a pair of long pants covered with impressionistic patches, and a pair of disreputable shoes. An old vest hangs unbuttoned on his shoulders.*

[65]

GREAT CÆSAR

GEORGE's *innocent moon face wears a baffled frown most of the time; he never quite catches up.*)

JOE (*who is pounding heavily on a sign by which he is seated in the center of the floor as the curtain rises*). Is this the way you want the signs fixed, Harry?

HARRY (*at front right, looking up from the sign he is painting*). Yep. That's all right, Joe. Be sure to make it solid.

JOE. This is solid enough, all right.

BILLY (*watching over GEORGE's shoulder as he paints at front left*). George, you poor fish! Harry, I told you he couldn't paint this sign. Look how he's spelled " Julius."

GEORGE (*sullenly*). What's the matter with it?

BILLY. Julius Cæsar wouldn't recognize his own name the way you have it spelled, that's what is the matter with it.

GEORGE. Aw, what difference does the spelling make?

BILLY. You don't expect people to come to our show if they can't read the signs, do you?

GEORGE. It's not as bad as that. You can tell what it's meant to be.

HARRY (*working industriously*). Be quiet, you two.

BILLY. Well, Harry, this sign is awful.

HARRY. What's the matter with it, Billy?

BILLY. Come see for yourself.

HARRY (*crossing stage*). Here, give me a look at it, George. (*The sign is handed to him; he reads*

[66]

it and laughs.) Cæsar's ghost will haunt you for this, George.

JOE. Let me see it, Harry. (HARRY *holds sign so* JOE—*and the audience—can read. In rough letters it reads "GULUS."*) Good-night, George, what's that meant to be?

GEORGE. Julius. G-u-l-u-s, Julius. (*Boys laugh.*) Well, that's one way to spell it, I guess.

BILLY. See, Harry, I told you he couldn't do it. Let me paint the sign.

HARRY. Then what will we let George do?

BILLY. Let him watch me and learn something.

GEORGE. I want more than that to do.

HARRY. I know; we'll let George carry up the boards and make the seats. How's that, George?

GEORGE. Suits me all right. I don't like sign painting anyhow. (*Frowning at* BILLY.) It's kind of a baby job.   [*Goes out rear left.*

BILLY (*briskly*). What do you want on here?

HARRY. Oh, just an announcement like this one. (*Holds up sign and reads.*) "Big Show—Julius Cæsar—This Afternoon—In Joe's Barn—Five Cents."

BILLY. I'll show old George how to do this.

(*As the boys are working in silence,* JANE, JOE'S *eleven-year-old sister, comes in rear left, followed by* LUCILLE, *her equal in years, but not in assurance.*)

JANE. See, Lucille, what did I tell you? I knew they would be here in the haymow. (*Proceeding unabashed by her silent reception.*) Say, what are you doing with all this red paint?

BILLY. Couldn't you guess?—We're—painting.

JANE (*piqued*). Well, you better not slop it around so freely. George is all splotched up with it until he looks like a murderer.

BILLY. He's been murdering the English language. Look how he spelled " Julius."

LUCILLE. Oh, what is that sign for?

(*A moment of discouraging silence.*)

JANE (*persistently*). What are you boys up to?

JOE. Sis, can't you see we're busy? Beat it and let us alone.

LUCILLE (*cautiously*). Come on, Jane, we better go.

JANE (*amused*). Oh, ho! Anyone could tell you don't have any brothers. I never pay any attention to what Joe says. And I've as much right in Father's haymow as he has.

JOE. Maybe you have, but be quiet and don't bother us now.

JANE (*after looking over* BILLY's *shoulder*). Oh, Lucille, I know what they're going to do. They're giving a play. Aren't you, Harry?

(GEORGE *has come in with planks; is building seats on boxes at left of stage.*)

HARRY. Yep.

LUCILLE. Oh, yes, and these are to be the seats. Oh, Jane, this makes a grand theatre, doesn't it?

JANE. Yes, it's fine.

LUCILLE (*aside*). I wonder if maybe they would let us be in the show too.

JANE. Sure. They'll have to. I'll make 'em.

LUCILLE (*amazed*). How can you do that?

GREAT CÆSAR

JANE. You just watch me. Harry, we want to be in the play too.

JOE. Now there's no use in starting that. We're not going to give a show with girls in it, and that's final.

BILLY. I should say so. This is the play of " Julius Cæsar "; it's all about men; there aren't any women in it.

JANE. I guess there are. Julius Cæsar had a wife, didn't he, Lucille?

(HARRY *looks up and listens quietly and thoughtfully.*)

LUCILLE. Yes, I think he did. And the other man, Brutus, he had a wife, too.

(GEORGE, *bringing in a plank, stops to listen.*)

JOE. We're not going to have any wives in this play, so you might as well beat it.

HARRY (*arising*). Just wait a minute, Joe. I think we can use the girls. Cæsar's wife Calpurnia and Brutus's wife Portia are important in the story. Why not have the girls take those parts?

JOE (*cheerfully*). If you say so it's all right with me. You're getting up the show.

LUCILLE. You'll let us, won't you, Harry? Please.

JANE. You need us, don't you?

HARRY (*flattered*). Sure. We're short a few characters, anyway.

JOE. It's all right with me, then. (*The girls whisper together in delight.*) But what were you going to do about those characters before the girls came?

HARRY. I thought maybe you or George could be the women.

JOE. Oh, no, I don't want to be a woman. I'd rather let the girls stay.

HARRY. All right, that's what we'll do.

GEORGE (*slamming down a plank, vociferously*). I won't be a woman!

BILLY. Oh, be quiet. You don't have to. It's all settled now.

JOE (*drawing* HARRY *aside*). There's one thing, Harry, to think about. We won't give them a share of the money, will we?

HARRY (*aside*). No, I should say not. This is our show; we thought it up. They don't need any money anyhow.

LUCILLE (*coming forward*). Harry, you'll have to teach us our parts. I don't know a thing about this play.

JANE. I don't know much about it myself. But I can do it if you'll tell me.

HARRY. All right, we're going to have a rehearsal now. First we'll have to put out the signs to draw a crowd. Is your sign ready, Billy?

BILLY. All done. (*Holds it up.*) How's that, George?

(GEORGE *makes a face at the sign.*)

HARRY (*gathering up signs*). Here, George, you hang 'em on the fence. And hurry back.

GEORGE (*as he goes out front left*). All right.

HARRY. Now this is the stage (*Pointing to an*

[70]

improvised platform of boards and boxes at right of stage.) and these are the entrances. (*Points to right front and right rear entrances.*)

JANE. Where's the curtain?

HARRY. There isn't any.

JANE. Oughtn't you to have one?

HARRY. No. I read that Shakespeare never had any curtains or footlights, so I guess we can get along without them.

GEORGE (*entering front left*). Better hurry with your rehearsal. There are three kids down there now waiting to get in, and two more went home to get their nickels.

JOE. Good. We'll make some money on this.

BILLY. We will if we ever get ready to let 'em in. Come on, let's start.

JANE. Yes, I think so. What parts do you want us girls to take?

HARRY. We haven't decided that yet. Let me see—Joe, you better be Julius Cæsar.

JOE. No, I don't want to be the leading guy. I can't remember all the speeches.

HARRY. You don't have to say much. It's an easy part. We kill you, and ——

JOE (*in alarm*). Oh, you kill me, do you ——

HARRY. Well, we pretend to kill you, and then all you have to do is lie still while Brutus and Antony make speeches about you.

JOE. Oh, that's all right. I'll be Julius.

BILLY (*maliciously*). Better let George do that part—he'd be good on that lying still, and looking dead.

GEORGE. Aw, you shut up.

GREAT CÆSAR

HARRY. I'm saving George for another part. Billy, you can be Brutus, and I'll be Antony. We're the ones that make the great speeches.

JANE. But where do we come in?

HARRY. You're the Roman ladies. Lucille, you can be Calpurnia.

LUCILLE. Calpurnia? Who was she?

HARRY. Calpurnia was Cæsar's wife.

JOE. I don't want her for a wife. Is it absolutely necessary for Cæsar to have a wife in this play?

HARRY. It's absolutely necessary.

JOE. Well, if I have to have a wife, let my sister be it.

HARRY (*shortly*). All right. Anything to please you.

JANE. But then what will Lucille be?

HARRY. She can be Portia, Brutus's wife.

JOE. Now we're all fixed except George.

GEORGE. Yes, what am I?

HARRY. You'll have a very important part. You remember in this story there's a mob of people who listen to the speeches, and then start out after Brutus?

GEORGE. Yes.

HARRY. Well, George, you're the mob.

GEORGE. Am I the whole mob? All by myself?

HARRY. Sure.

GEORGE. It will be a hard part, but I guess I can take it all right.

BILLY. Oh, that's rich. He looks like a mob, sure enough.

GREAT CÆSAR

JOE. Come on, now, Harry, and tell us about our parts.

HARRY. All right. You all sit down here and listen and I'll explain it to you. (*They sit on the benches*, HARRY *sits before them on a box.*) We can't give the whole play because it's too long, so we'll just take the best parts. There will be two scenes. In the first Brutus talks to Portia and tells her he's going to kill Cæsar, and then when Cæsar comes in, Brutus stabs him dead.

BILLY. What do I stab him with?

HARRY. A dagger, of course.

BILLY. But I haven't any dagger.

HARRY. Make yourself one out of a piece of board. Don't bother me with that now until I get through telling you your parts.—After Brutus stabs Cæsar, he goes away with the mob following after him to hear his speech.

BILLY. I don't want that mob following me around.

HARRY (*irritably*). He's going to anyway, so shut up until I get through. (*More calmly.*)— Then Antony, that's me, comes in and finds Cæsar's body and he carries it to the public square ——

BILLY. How are you going to carry Cæsar's body?

HARRY. How do you suppose they carried dead Cæsar's body? On a funeral bier, of course.

LUCILLE. What's a funeral bier?

HARRY. It's something to carry a dead person on—I guess it's something like a stretcher.

JANE. You don't have a stretcher. What are you going to use?

[73]

GREAT CÆSAR

HARRY. You never mind that. I'll find some way to carry Cæsar's body.—Now, what was I telling you?

LUCILLE. About Antony coming in, finding dead Cæsar's body, and carrying it to the public square.

HARRY. Oh, yes. Well, Antony comes to the public square where Brutus is telling the mob that he killed Cæsar because he was too ambitious. The mob yells for Brutus and when he asks 'em if he has offended any of 'em the mob says " None, Brutus, none."—Can you say that, Mob?

GEORGE (*arising, speaking pompously*). None, Brutus, none.

HARRY. All right. Then Antony makes a speech to the mob and persuades them to turn against Brutus.

GEORGE. What do I say in that part?

HARRY. Never mind that now. I'm going to tell each one of you exactly what to say while we're getting our costumes on. We want to get just the plot outline now, so we know what we're trying to do.—The last scene will show the mob killing Brutus. You chase him across the stage—and kill him.

JOE. How does the mob kill Brutus?

HARRY. Oh, any way will do.—Choke him to death. That always looks well on the stage.

BILLY. But why do I have to be choked to death? It's not that way in the real play.

HARRY. I know it. But we can't show all those battle scenes, and after the mob gets all worked up by Antony's speech, you ought to let it kill you. That will make a nice ending to the play.

[74]

GREAT CÆSAR

BILLY. All right. (*Aside to* LUCILLE.) That mob will have to go some to catch me, that's all.

A VOICE OUTSIDE (*left stage*). Hey, when does your show begin?

JOE. We better open the door, or they'll go away.

HARRY. You let the audience in, Joe, and the rest of you go put on your costumes.

(JOE *goes out front left.*)

LUCILLE. Are you going to have costumes?

GEORGE. Sure, we have to look like Romers, don't we?

JANE. Romans, you mean. What costumes have you got?

BILLY. Come and see for yourself. They're swell.   [JANE, BILLY, LUCILLE, *exit from right.*

JOE (*entering front left*). There are about a dozen kids down there. One of us will have to stand at the door to collect the money.

GEORGE. Oh, Harry, let me do it.

HARRY. No, none of us can do it, or the show will be late. We ought to be getting dressed right now.

JOE. Then we'll have to get a boy out of the crowd to be doorkeeper.

HARRY. All right. You pick one out and get him started. (JOE *goes out again.*) Come on, George. I have to get you dressed up like a mob.

GEORGE. Let me wear that long robe, will you?

HARRY. We'll try it on and see how it looks.

(HARRY *and* GEORGE *exit right front. Off stage to left a clamor is heard.* " *When do you start?* "

" Hey, let us in." " Hurry up with your show."
Joe *reënters front left with* Sam.)

Joe.   Now, Sam, all you have to do is to stand
here and collect the money as they come in.

Sam.   Sure.   What do you charge them?

Joe.   A nickel, cash down, no credit.

Sam.   Suppose a guy hasn't any money.   Shall
I throw him out?

Joe.   I don't know.—Wait a minute, I'll ask.—
Oh, Harry!

Harry (*coming in front right half garbed for
play*).   What do you want?

Joe.   Charge everybody a nickel, whether he has
it or not?

Harry.   No, you can't do that.   There may be
some deserving cases you'll have to admit free.   All
shows do that.   [*Exits right front.*

Sam.   All right.   Deserving cases free.   All
others five cents cash.   Let's go.

Joe.   I'll go down and let them in gradually.

[*Exits front left.*

Sam (*looking out front left*).   Have your change
ready.   Five cents.

A Girl (*paying her nickel*).   Don't you have
any reserved seats?

Sam.   They're all reserved.   Take your choice.
(*Seizing a passing patron.*)   Wait a minute, here.
Where's your nickel?

A Small Boy (*alarmed*).   Nickel?   I haven't
any.   I just followed the crowd.

Sam.   So you haven't a nickel?   Well, what do
you have?

GREAT CÆSAR

SMALL BOY. I have a banana. (*He holds it up for inspection.*)

SAM (*after smelling the banana*). This seems to me like a deserving case. (*Slips banana in pocket.*) Go on in, kid.

(*Several children come in and pay their nickels. SAM collects with great gusto and enlivens his duties by crying out " Five cents," " Have your change ready " and " Step forward, please " in a most professional manner.*)

A GIRL (*coming in front left holding a stick of candy*). How much is the show?

SAM. What is that, candy?

GIRL. Yes. How much does the show cost?

SAM (*seizing candy from her*). Nothing. It's free. (*As the girl hesitates, he shoves her to a seat.*) Step forward, please.

JOE (*entering front left*). That's about all just now. I think there are some coming down the street, but I have to go and get dressed. Were there any deserving cases?

SAM (*who has hidden the candy and banana in his pocket quickly*). Two so far. (*Piously.*) I just didn't have the heart to turn them away.

JOE. All right. But don't let too many in free. It will eat up the profits. [JOE *exits front right.*

(*Two more boys enter front left and pay for seats. These fellows are well equipped with paper wads and rubbers. At intervals during the play they take shots at the actors.*)

HARRY (*entering back right garbed as ANTONY.*

[77]

GREAT CÆSAR

His costume comprises a bright bath robe, a dark felt hat with broad rolled brim and long white feather, a cane, and an eyeglass). Ladies and gentlemen. We are about to present the great play of Julius Cæsar. The first scene will be the assassination of Cæsar. (*He goes out amid applause and whistling.*)

(BILLY *and* LUCILLE *enter front right as* BRUTUS *and* PORTIA. BILLY *wears an old derby, a bright-colored cape, a pair of long trousers and he carries a wooden sword.* LUCILLE *wears a long dress with a sweeping train, a shawl, an old-fashioned bonnet tied under her chin with a bow of ribbons. She carries a large work bag and knitting. They seat themselves on the edge of the improvised platform.* PORTIA *begins her knitting;* BRUTUS *industriously whets his sword on the sole of his shoe. He tests his work by running his thumb along the edge and by chopping at a hair which he has jerked unceremoniously from* PORTIA'S *head. Satisfied with his weapon, he meditates gloomily for a moment.*)

BRUTUS. Say, Portia.

PORTIA. Yes, Brutus.

BRUTUS (*with Roman sternness*). You know that fellow Julius Cæsar?

PORTIA (*nodding*). Yes, Brutus.

BRUTUS. Well, I'm going to kill him.

PORTIA. Brutus, you oughtn't to do that. He might not like it.

BRUTUS. I'm afraid he won't, but just the same I'm going to kill him this morning. Some of us Romans decided that he's putting on too many airs.

Next thing you know he'll be making himself a king,
and then he'll raise the taxes.

PORTIA. Brutus, I thought you liked Cæsar.

BRUTUS. I do like him, he's a good old scout,
but I will not pay any more taxes.

PORTIA. Oh, Brutus, how determined you are.
If you've made up your mind, I suppose you'll do it.

BRUTUS. Yes, and I'm going to do it this morn-
ing, just as sure as my name is Lepidus Popilius
Trebonius Ligarius Claudius Artemidorus Decius
Brutus.

PORTIA. Well, if you must kill him, be careful
not to get any blood on that new suit.

(*A loud blast on a fish horn resounds off stage
right.*)

BRUTUS. Hush, woman, here comes Cæsar.

(*Enter HARRY as ANTONY, JOE as CÆSAR, JANE
as CALPURNIA, followed by GEORGE as the MOB.
They come in the back right, ANTONY leading and
blowing a flourish on his fish horn, CÆSAR and CAL-
PURNIA on his arm, and the MOB trailing respect-
fully in the rear. CÆSAR wears a bath robe girt
with a wide, brilliant red sash. He has a tin funnel
on his head by way of crown; a toy policeman's club
is his badge of authority. CALPURNIA is clad in a
long dress with sweeping ain, and a lace curtain
veil, pinned to her head, hangs down her back. She
wears long gloves and carries a lorgnette, which she
employs with a royal gesture. The MOB wears a
horse blanket loosely fastened about him with a
rope; his head is uncovered and his hair tousled,
and he carries a broomstick staff.*)

GREAT CÆSAR

ANTONY. Make way for most noble Cæsar.

MOB. Stand back and give him air.

(*A paper wad hits* CÆSAR *but he does not deign to notice.*)

CÆSAR. Good-morning, Brutus.

BRUTUS (*in surly tone*). Hello.

CALPURNIA (*going over, shaking hands*). How are you, Mrs. Brutus?

PORTIA (*moving over to make a seat for* CALPURNIA). I'm fine, Mrs. Cæsar. How's all your folks? (*They converse quietly.*)

CÆSAR (*imperiously*). Antony! Ho, Antony!

ANTONY (*with low obeisance*). Yes, most noble Cæsar.

CÆSAR. That fellow Brutus looks gloomy this morning. I wonder what's the matter with him.

ANTONY. I hear that he's worrying about his taxes, sir.

CÆSAR. He oughtn't to worry about taxes. He's rich, isn't he?

ANTONY. I'll say so. He has three automobiles and a radio set, and he owns a lot of candy factories.

CÆSAR. Then he has no business looking so sour.

ANTONY. I think you should speak to him about it, your honor. He sets a bad example for the mob. They'll be wanting free movies next.

CÆSAR (*approaching* BRUTUS). Brutus, you are too gloomy to suit me. If you don't cheer up, I'll put you in jail.

BRUTUS (*leaping up*). Never. You expect to become a king, don't you?

[80]

CÆSAR. Sure thing. I'm going to run for it at the next election; all the Democrats are for me.

BRUTUS. Well, I'm not. You shall never, never, never be king. I'll kill you first.—Take that. (*Stabs him in stomach.*)

CÆSAR. Ouch. Oh, Calpurnia, I fear I am killed.

CALPURNIA. Cheer up, Cæsar, it might be worse.

(ANTONY *dodges the tumult and runs off stage rear right.*)

BRUTUS. Take that too. (*Stabs again.*)

CÆSAR. Ouch. Oh, I am dead. (*Falls.*)

CALPURNIA (*wringing hands*). Now see what you have done, Brutus. What a shame. He was the best husband I ever had.

MOB (*running around body in lamentation*). Oh! Oh! Oh! Oh!

BRUTUS (*holding up his hand to* MOB). Peace, my countrymen. Just follow me until I can find a soap box, and I'll tell you a few reasons why I killed Cæsar.

MOB. Come on, Brutus, I know where there's a soap box.

(*Exit* MOB, *followed by* BRUTUS *and* PORTIA, *front right.*)

CALPURNIA (*surveying* CÆSAR, *stamping foot*). This is enough to make anyone lose her temper.

ANTONY (*entering rear right with wheelbarrow, which he brings alongside the body*). Poor Cæsar ain't what he used to be, is he?

[81]

CALPURNIA. No, I'm afraid they've spoiled him. (*Angrily.*) But what are you going to do about it? I thought you were a friend of his and then just when you were needed, you ran off.

ANTONY. I remembered some business. (*A paper wad hits* ANTONY.) Now I have made a plan. I'm going to take Cæsar's body down to the public square where Brutus is making a speech to the mob. You just watch me. I'll get that mob after Brutus, and they'll muss him up worse than he did Cæsar.

CALPURNIA. That's a good idea. Come on, let's go.

(*They load* CÆSAR *on wheelbarrow and exit rear right,* ANTONY *having much trouble with the wheelbarrow.*)

HARRY (*reëntering immediately in costume*). Ladies and gentlemen, this concludes the first act. (*Applause, cheers and whistling from the audience.*) I regret to state that during the performance of this sublime dramatic spectacle some low-minded person was observed shooting paper wads in the direction of the distinguished members of the cast. If this despicable outrage continues, the mob himself, who weighs 140 pounds, will cross the footlights and forcibly and with malice aforethought will sit on the offender. (*Pointing suddenly and directly to the culprits.*) Do you hear that?

ONE OF THE ACCUSED. It wasn't me, honest.

HARRY (*again the suave manager*). Ladies and gentlemen, the next and last scene will portray the famous orations of Brutus and Antony, and the play will close with the execution of Brutus at the hands of the mob. I thank you.

[Exit, amid applause.

BRUTUS (*entering front right carrying soap box*). Here's a good place for a speech. (*Puts box on platform and ascends.*)

PORTIA. Be careful, Brutus, don't fall.

MOB. Hooray for Brutus.

BRUTUS. Romans, members of this mob, I promised to tell you why I stabbed Cæsar, and that's what I'm going to do—if I don't fall off.

MOB. You tell 'em, Brutus.

BRUTUS. I killed Cæsar because he was ambitious to become a king and raise the taxes. He was my friend, we belonged to the same lodge, but because he was ambitious (*Pantomiming the historic stroke.*) I stabbed him in the solar plexis in the morning in the year of 44 B. C.

MOB. Atta boy, Brutus, atta boy.

BRUTUS. Has that offended any of you? If so, speak up.

MOB (*after a moment of panic*). None, Brutus, none.

(ANTONY *enters rear right with* CÆSAR's *body, followed by* CALPURNIA.)

ANTONY. Come down off that soap box and give me a chance. I want to make a speech now.

BRUTUS. All right, Antony, I'm through, anyway.

ANTONY (*ascending soap box*). Friends, Romans, countrymen. Lend me your ears. I have brought Cæsar's dead body here to preach the funeral sermon

[83]

about it. If you have tears, prepare to shed them now. (*The* Mob *shakes out a bandana and hangs it over his arm.*) Look at poor Cæsar, who was once so powerful, now lying cold and dead——

(*At this moment the corpse is vitalized by the stinging impact of a deftly-aimed paper wad.*)

CÆSAR (*sitting up in the wheelbarrow*). Ow. Who hit me with that paper wad?

MOB (*thrusting* CÆSAR *back*). Calm yourself, Cæsar. (*To audience.*) I'll catch you next time. (*To* ANTONY.) Go on, Antony, I'm listening.

ANTONY. As I was saying, look at poor dead Cæsar. Not only is he dead, but look at his clothes. All ripped, absolutely ruined!

MOB. That's right, they are. What a shame.

ANTONY. And why did Brutus do this? He says Cæsar was ambitious but it was not so. It wasn't Cæsar who was ambitious, it was Brutus. He killed Cæsar (*Levels an accusing finger at* BRUTUS.) so that he could be king.

MOB. Oh, the villain! Just wait till I catch him. I'll choke the life out of him.

(*Pandemonium ensues.* BRUTUS *dodges the* MOB *and exits front right, followed by* MOB, PORTIA, ANTONY, *and* CALPURNIA, *leaving* CÆSAR *in his wheelbarrow. At the applause that follows he sits up and looks around, then gets up and pushes off wheelbarrow front right amid cheers.* BRUTUS *enters rear right, pursued by* MOB, *who steps on the edge of his robe, stumbles and misses in the chase.* BRUTUS *exits front right, followed by* MOB.)

GREAT CÆSAR

HARRY (*reappearing back left*). Ladies and gentlemen, we regret to announce that we will be unable to complete the play. (*The audience hisses and jeers.*) We regret to omit the beautiful and touching episode which depicts the choking of Brutus by the mob, but Brutus has run off and the mob can't find him anywhere. (SAM *slinks out front left.*) This concludes our performance. (*He bows and exits rear right; audience files out front left.*)

JOE (*crossing stage from front right, to last of audience*). Where's Sam?

A BOY. He went down-stairs first of all.

JOE. Tell him to wait a minute, will you?

BOY. Sure, I'll tell him.

(GEORGE *and girls, having discarded their stage costumes, enter front right.*)

JANE (*scolding as they enter*). You should have caught Brutus, anyway. That made a bad ending to the play, not to have the choking scene.

GEORGE. I tried to catch him, I tell you. It was his fault; he shouldn't have run so fast.

BILLY (*appearing rear left*). Aha, you couldn't catch me, could you?

(GEORGE *chases* BILLY *around the stage.*)

JANE (*seizing* BILLY). You little rascal, what did you mean by running away? You spoiled the show.

(HARRY *enters quietly at front right, listens.*)

[85]

BILLY. The show was ruined anyway before I ran away.

GEORGE. How was it ruined? If you had let me choke you it would have been a success.

BILLY. No, it couldn't have been. Cæsar spoiled it when he came to life.

LUCILLE. I thought so too. It was all ridiculous after that.

JOE. That paper wad didn't feel ridiculous, I'll tell you. Did you think I was going to lie there and be a target? And I wasn't the only ridiculous one, either.

BILLY. I'll admit that it was ridiculous when that big mob couldn't catch me.

GEORGE (*advancing*). I have a notion to choke you now, you ——

HARRY (*coming between*). Here, quit this fussing. Let's divide our money; that will make us feel better.

JOE. That's the idea. George, Sam's waiting down-stairs. You run down and tell him to turn the money over to you.

GEORGE (*going out front left*). All right.

JANE. You didn't tell us about the money part. I suppose you'll divide it equally?

LUCILLE. Oh, how much do you suppose we'll get?

HARRY (*hedging*). Well, girls, Joe and I have talked this matter over and we decided,—that is, we thought—Joe, she's your sister, you tell 'em what we thought.

JOE (*fearful*). Harry thought it would be best, since we were the ones who thought up the show, if we would—(*Stops, then smiles weakly.*) count the money first, and then divide it afterward.

(*The girls whisper to one another in anticipation.*)

HARRY (*aside to* JOE). That's no good way to settle it, Joe. You'll have to tell 'em that they don't get any of the money and you might as well tell 'em now.

JOE. Wait till we count it and give me a chance to think up something.

(GEORGE *enters left with hands in pockets.*)

BILLY. Well, old Mob, how much money is there?
GEORGE (*in tragic tones*). None, Brutus, none!
HARRY. What do you mean?
GEORGE. Sam ran off with the money.
BILLY. Great Cæsar!

(*The curtain falls swiftly before a picture of despair.*)

FALSE PRETENSES

"False Pretenses" was first produced at Dennis Junior High School, Richmond, Indiana, in December, 1922, with the following cast:

HARRY	REXFORD HUNTINGTON
DAN	HAROLD GREEN
SHORTY	HERSCHEL CLEVENGER
BILL	DUDLEY CARTWRIGHT
JACK	RALPH STEELE
RED	FRANKLYN WALLS
KATHLEEN	EDITH JOHNSON
PEGGY	KATHRYN WEIMER
MARIE	JANE KNOLLENBERG
RUTH	MARIE MACKEY
FRANCES	MARGARET GRANT

FALSE PRETENSES

SCENE:—*The library room of an ordinary public school; the time is at noon intermission of a school day. Doors open into the library from classrooms on either side. Double doors in the center open into a corridor which runs parallel with the rear wall of the scene. Along this rear wall, on both sides of the double doors, are well-filled bookcases. There are three reading tables, each surrounded by its disorderly array of chairs, but the room is not crowded, and there is open floor space across the entire front stage.*

(*As the curtain rises it discloses five boys: JACK, twelve; BILL, twelve; SHORTY, eleven; DAN, thirteen; and HARRY, fourteen; seated around a table at right stage, engaged in an earnest discussion over a disheveled newspaper.*)

JACK (*searching his pockets*). Thirty-seven cents, that's as much as I can raise. What have you got, Bill?

BILL. Two dimes.

SHORTY. I'll chip in forty cents, but that's my entire fortune.

BILL. This is a poor crowd since that last carnival. I wish I had the two dollars I spent trying to win a box of candy.

DAN. Yes, and I wish I had the dollar I lost there.

FALSE PRETENSES

HARRY. Wishing won't get us the money, and this sporting goods sale won't last forever. If we are going to buy anything, we'll have to get busy. Let's make a list and see how much we have and what we want.

JACK. That's the idea. Here, I'll read the list of articles on sale. Shorty, you put 'em down; that is, what we think we can afford. (*Reading from newspaper.*) Pitcher's mit—seventy-five cents; Ty Cobb bat—one dollar and seventy-five cents;— and I guess we ought to have this catcher's mit— one dollar and forty cents ——

BILL (*looking over* JACK's *shoulder*). We want that Big League baseball, special at eighty cents.

JACK. What's that total, Shorty?

SHORTY (*laboriously*). Five, five, ten, eight, nine, thirteen, twenty-seven, three, four—$4.70.

DAN (*hopelessly*). That settles it. That's more money than this crowd ever had.

BILL. Let's see where we stand, anyway. Jack, how much?

JACK (*emphatically*). Thirty-seven cents.

(BILL *notes answers.*)

BILL. Shorty?

SHORTY. Forty cents.

BILL. Dan?

DAN (*sullenly*). Thirty cents.

HARRY. Is that what you have or how you feel?

DAN. Both.

BILL. Well, Harry, how much?

HARRY. I'm the wealthiest fellow here.

[92]

FALSE PRETENSES

BILL (*hopefully*). Why didn't you tell us you were flush? How much?

HARRY (*laughing as he dashes their hopes*). Forty-five cents.

BILL. Aw, that's not so much. That's not enough. (*Struggles with the figures.*) And with my twenty cents—hum—makes a total of $1.72.

HARRY. Just what do we lack then, Shorty?

SHORTY (*figuring obediently*). $1.72 from $4.70 —leave $2.98.

JACK. Hopeless. Hopeless.

DAN. $2.98! (*Scornfully.*) Where could we ever raise that much?

SHORTY (*practically*). That's the question. But we might as well raise it because there won't be another chance like this for a year. It wouldn't be economical for us to pass up this sale.

HARRY. You're right, Shorty, it wouldn't. Aren't we always being taught to be thrifty? Where's a better chance to save money than by buying at this sale?

SHORTY. Maybe we can borrow the money somewhere and pay it back later.

DAN. Where are we to borrow, I'd like to know. My credit's no good, I'll tell you.

BILL. Neither's mine.

JACK. Maybe some of the girls have some money. We might ask 'em.

DAN. That idea's no good. You might ask 'em all day and you would still lack the $2.98.

BILL. They wouldn't lend to this crowd. They're too cautious.

DAN. That's a fact. They know us too well.

FALSE PRETENSES

HARRY. But if we told 'em what it was for don't you suppose they would help us?

BILL. No, they would say we don't need any new stuff. They think you can have a real ball game with a barrel stave and little sister's red rubber ball.

HARRY. Listen, then; borrow the money from them without saying what it's for.

JACK. You would never get it without telling them something.

HARRY (*thoughtfully*). Well—then, tell them something.

JACK. What will you tell them?

HARRY. Tell them their money's worth; it doesn't necessarily need to be the truth; they'll be just as happy as long as they don't know better.

JACK. I believe that's a good idea, Harry.

DAN. You mean make up some sort of a tale on which to borrow the money, and then pay them back before they find out what the money really went for?

HARRY. Yes, that's it. If they won't give for buying baseball supplies, they might give for something else.

SHORTY. That's what you would call getting money under false pretenses, I guess.

HARRY. Oh, I suppose it is, but it wouldn't do any harm. The money would be used for a good purpose, wouldn't it, and then as soon as we could raise the $2.98, perhaps by the first of next week, we could give back every cent we had taken from the girls.

JACK. Yes, it would be just humoring their foolish ideas. I'm in favor of trying it.

FALSE PRETENSES

SHORTY. Oh, I'm not objecting. I'll try it, if the rest of you want to.

BILL. Sure, we can work it easy.

HARRY. Yes, and there's no harm in it. But now we'll have to decide what sort of a pretense we can make. What shall we tell 'em?

SHORTY. It will have to be something that will appeal to girls, whatever that would be.

JACK. Something silly, no doubt.

BILL. Something sympathetic would do it. Dad tells Mother you can get money from any woman by working on her sympathies. He says any rusty looking tramp can put up a hard luck story and get all the spare change out of Mother's pocket-book. It's so, too.

SHORTY. That's about right. Just look how the girls will shell out their money to send flowers to someone who has sore throat, or a sprained ankle.

HARRY (*springing up*). There's the very thing. Why can't we tell the girls we're buying the flowers for some sick pupil?

JACK. That sounds right enough.

(*Others nod assent.*)

BILL. But who would be the sick person? Who is absent to-day?

SHORTY. Charley is absent.

DAN. Charley wouldn't do. He's tardy about half the time and he might walk in on us this afternoon, and then where would we be?

JACK. That's right. Well, Sarah hasn't been here for two days; what's the matter with her?

DAN. I don't know, but the girls would. They

would know something was wrong if we said we were sending flowers to a girl. We'll have to play safe and use a boy.

BILL. I know the one. Red Smith! He'll be absolutely safe, because he left town this morning with his uncle.

SHORTY. That's right. They are driving to the state fair and they won't be back until the middle of next week. That will give us time to raise the money and settle with the girls.

DAN. Yes, Red will be safe enough. He is probably a hundred miles from here by now. I saw that old red head of his about a square away this morning, bouncing along in his uncle's car—I guess they were starting off then.

HARRY. All right, it couldn't be any better. Red's the one. Now, we ought to draw up a regular subscription list, so that the girls can see where we have signed our names, and can see that it's all perfectly square and regular.

DAN. So that the girls can see that it is what it ain't, you mean.

HARRY. Well, you know what I mean. Shorty, you have the pencil; you draw up the preamble and be secretary. I'll be treasurer and hold the coin.

BILL. How do you get that? (*Jumping up.*) I think I ought to be treasurer.

HARRY (*leaping to his feet in defense*). Didn't I put in the most money, and didn't I think up the scheme of sending flowers?

SHORTY (*calmly*). You put in a few more cents than the rest of us, but as for the scheme, we all thought up that.

FALSE PRETENSES

DAN. Oh, let Bill be treasurer, and you be the president. That's a better job.

HARRY. All right. Shorty, what have you got written down?

SHORTY. Subscription list.

DAN. You'll have to write a lot of stuff to make it sound impressive.

SHORTY. You tell me how to start it, then.

DAN. I'm not certain whether this is correct, but I think we ought to start with a " whereas." Dad was reading a list of revolutions he made up for a meeting, and ——

HARRY. Resolutions, you mean.

DAN. Yes, that's it, resolutions. They all start with " whereas " and string out forever. You ought to use all the long words you can; that will go big with the girls and they'll hand over the money.

JACK. If you know so much about it, Dan, start him off and let him write it down.

DAN. Well, start like this—" Whereas, our well-known and highly esteemed fellow-pupil, Red Smith, has fell a victim to—to ——" What did he fall a victim to, Harry?

HARRY. To insidious disease. I heard a fellow say that in a speech, and the way he used it, it must be something terrible.

DAN. That's all right, that's hot stuff.—" has fell a victim to insidious disease ——"

SHORTY. How do you spell it, Harry?

HARRY. Don't ask me. Use your imagination.

DAN. Ready?—" and—and—whereas we, the fellow-pupils of the aforesaid Red Smith, hereinafter referred to as the diseased, do—do ——" (*Break-*

[97]

FALSE PRETENSES

ing off.) Say, I'm not going to do all this work. What do we do, Bill?

BILL. " do heartily lament the diseased condition of the diseased and wish to—wish to ——"

HARRY. " wish to express our sorrowing sympathy for the unfortunate diseased, therefor be it resolved, enacted and declared that—that ——" What do we resolve, Jack?

JACK. " That we shall raise $4.70 to buy a ball, a bat, a ——"

SHORTY. Wait, you bonehead, I can't put that down; you'll give it all away.

DAN. " We shall raise $4.70 to buy a bouquet of flowers to—to ——"

HARRY. " to present to the diseased in—in ——"

BILL. " in token of—of ——"

JACK. " our sympathy for his disease."

SHORTY. Then across the bottom I'll put "Amen, so be it."

HARRY. Read it all; let's hear how it sounds.

SHORTY (*arising, reading impressively*). " Whereas, our well known and highly steamed fellow pupil Red Smith has fell a victim to (*Hesitatingly.*) in-sid-i-ous ——" (*Looks questioningly at* HARRY.)

HARRY (*nodding*). That's right.

SHORTY (*reading*). " In-sid-i-ous disease, and whereas we, the fellow-pupils of the aforesaid Red Smith, hereinafter referred to as the diseased, do heartily lament the diseased condition of the diseased therefor be it resolved, acted, and declared ——"

HARRY. En-acted, e-n-a-c-t-e-d.

SHORTY (*frowning at paper*). Enacted? Oh,

yes, that's what I have. (*Makes a surreptitious correction.*) "enacted and declared that we shall raise $4.70 to buy a bouquet of flowers to present to the diseased in token of our sympathy for his disease. Amen, so be it."

HARRY. That's the stuff, all right.

SHORTY. Sign your names now, and give the money to the treasurer.

(*As they continue the conversation, the boys sign and pay.*)

JACK (*as he signs*). This ought to do the work.

DAN. And now we'll have to get the girls and rope 'em in on this.

BILL. Wait a minute; we'll have to agree on our story. What shall we say is the matter with Red?

HARRY. Oh,—appendicitis ——

DAN. Combined with mumps, chicken-pox, measles, and—and ——

SHORTY. And paralysis.

(*Boys nod approval.*)

HARRY. That ought to hold him for a week, at least. And when did he get sick?

DAN. Late last night, we'll say. (*Listens.*) Here comes someone. Make a long face, everyone, as though you're worried.

SHORTY. Stick to the story now, fellows, or we'll be wrecked.

(*The boys assume the most tragic expressions. PEGGY and MARIE enter right.*)

FALSE PRETENSES

PEGGY. Why, what's the matter with you, boys? You act as though you're at a funeral.

HARRY. Girls, we're afraid we may have to attend a funeral.

MARIE. What do you mean? Oh, tell us what's the matter.

DAN (*mournfully*). It's poor Red Smith. He's —he's very sick.

PEGGY. He is? He was in school yesterday. When was he taken sick?

SHORTY. Late last night—insidious disease laid him low.

MARIE. What's the matter with him?

SHORTY. Appendicitis.

(*Other boys follow rapidly.*)

BILL. With mumps ——

MARIE. What?

JACK. And chicken-pox ——

PEGGY. Really?

DAN. And measles ——

MARIE. Oh, dear.

HARRY (*hiding affected tears*). And paralysis.

PEGGY. How perfectly dreadful.

MARIE. Isn't it the most awful thing you ever heard of?

DAN. We're getting up a little subscription list to send him some flowers. Maybe you girls would like to be included.

PEGGY. Certainly I would.

MARIE. I'll be glad to contribute. How much are you trying to raise?

FALSE PRETENSES

Boys (*shouting almost in unison*). Two dollars and ninety-eight cents.

PEGGY. What? Are you going to buy the flowers at a bargain sale?

HARRY. We have raised a part of the money, you see, but we need $2.98 to make up the total of $4.70, which is the price of the flowers.

PEGGY. When did you price them?

SHORTY. Yesterday afternoon.

PEGGY. I thought Red didn't take sick until late last night.

SHORTY. Well, he didn't, but—you see—he ——

HARRY. He didn't look at all well yesterday and we—we were afraid he was going to be sick—so we priced the flowers.

MARIE. How thoughtful of you.

(PEGGY *and* MARIE *examine the resolutions and subscription list.*)

DAN (*to* HARRY). Yes, that was very thoughtful of you, Harry.

JACK. This is the resolution we have got up, and below is the place for you to sign your names. Bill is our treasurer; you may pay your money to him.

PEGGY. Are you sure Red is as sick as you think he is?

BILL. Peggy, if you only knew, you wouldn't ask.

DAN. That's right, you wouldn't.

PEGGY (*convinced*). I'm sorry. I'll give you seventy-five cents.

HARRY. That is very kind of you.

FALSE PRETENSES

MARIE. I'll give you a dollar. I just got it for spending money but poor Red needs all our sympathy now.

BILL. You are very generous, Marie.

(*As the girls write their subscriptions, after having delivered their money to* BILL, *the boys wink and nudge one another joyfully.* KATHLEEN, RUTH, *and* FRANCES *enter back from right, laughing and chatting.*)

FRANCES (*looking about*). Marie, what's gone wrong? Why are you all so solemn?

MARIE. Red Smith was taken very sick last night. He has—what is it, boys?

SHORTY (*mournfully*). Appendicitis.

(*Boys follow with hesitation.*)

BILL. With mumps.

JACK. And smallpox.—I mean chicken-pox.

DAN. And measles ——

HARRY. And paralysis.

RUTH. Oh, my, is there any hope for him?

BILL. We don't know, but we don't expect him here before the middle of next week.

KATHLEEN. Well, I should think not.

DAN (*absently*). I hope not.

KATHLEEN. What? Don't you want him to get well?

DAN. I mean—I mean—I hope he doesn't come back too soon and expose himself. He might take something else—pink eye, maybe.

KATHLEEN. I see. Oh, how dreadful he must

FALSE PRETENSES

feel. Can't we do something to cheer him up? We might send him some flowers.

JACK. We have prepared for that. Here are the resolutions of sympathy we have drawn up. If you want to help send him flowers, write your subscription here and pay Bill. He's our treasurer.

RUTH (*looking in purse*). Let me put down my name for seventy-five cents. Poor Red, how sorry I am for him.

KATHLEEN. Oh, I'd like to help. I'll give all I have, that's fifty cents.

FRANCES. I'll give a dollar. I wish I had more to give the poor boy.

DAN. Red will appreciate all this—if the flowers only get there in time.

FRANCES. Oh, is it as bad as all that? How awful.

JACK. Yes, the sooner you contribute, the more quickly we can buy the ball and bat and ——

RUTH. What?

JACK. I mean the flowers.

PEGGY. But you said ball and bat. What did you mean by that?

JACK (*floundering*). Well, I meant that—I meant what I was trying to say to mean—that I meant ——

KATHLEEN. Say it, say it.

HARRY. He doesn't know how to say it, that's all. This was the scheme. We thought that since Red is so fond of baseball we might have the flowers made up to represent a ball and bat. (*He gesticulates with frenzy and JACK follows his motions painfully, nodding.*)

FALSE PRETENSES

RUTH. A floral piece, you mean? But those are sent only to funerals.

(PEGGY *beckons significantly to* MARIE; *they whisper and leave stage right.*)

HARRY. That's right. We never thought of that, did we, Jack?

JACK. No, we never thought of that.

HARRY. You see, girls, we're so worried we can't think.

DAN. That's right. That's a fact.

FRANCES. You poor boys. Would you like to have us girls order the flowers for you?

BOYS (*shouting almost in unison*). Oh, no, no, no.

RUTH. But we would be so glad to do it and save you the worry.

DAN. When you talk that way you just cause us a lot more worry.

RUTH. Why?

SHORTY. You see, Ruth, you don't know about it.

DAN (*aside to* BILL). I'll say they don't. And I hope they never do.

BILL (*aside to* DAN). Shut up, you'll spoil everything.

KATHLEEN. I'm sure we know more about buying flowers than you do.

JACK. That wasn't what Shorty meant.

KATHLEEN. What did he mean, then?

JACK. Well,—I don't know. Ask him.

SHORTY. I meant you don't know what a peculiar case this is.

FALSE PRETENSES

FRANCES. What is so peculiar about this case?

BILL (*laboriously*). You see, girls, Red is very bashful. If he thought the flowers were picked out by girls he might be dangerously shocked.

HARRY. Yes, indeed, he'd be dangerously shocked if he heard anything about this affair.

DAN. That's right, too. That's a fact.

KATHLEEN. In that case, perhaps we had better not contribute our money.

BOYS (*almost in unison*). Oh, yes, yes.

HARRY. That will be all right.

KATHLEEN. But we don't want to give him a dangerous shock while he's ill.

HARRY. We'll arrange it so that he won't be shocked, if you'll just leave it to us. Now what flowers would you girls suggest? You know better than we do what would be suitable.

RUTH. Roses and carnations, I would say.

BILL. All right, that's what we'll get. (*Bell rings.*) There's the lunch bell now. Jack, we'll have time to run up town and attend to this business this noon. Let's go right away.

JACK. I'm ready to go any time, the sooner the better.

BILL. Thanks for your help and advice, girls. We'll get what you said.

[BILL *and* JACK *exit back to left.*

HARRY (*moving across stage*). Come on, fellows. I don't feel like eating, but we must keep up our strength.

DAN (*aside to* SHORTY). Yes, and keep up our nerve, too.

[105]

FALSE PRETENSES

SHORTY. Shh!

[HARRY, DAN, *and* SHORTY *exit left.*

RUTH. I hope Peggy and Marie stop here for us on their way to lunch. I suppose they will be too excited to remember.

FRANCES. How worried poor Red's mother must be.

KATHLEEN. How sick Red must be, with all those diseases at once.

(PEGGY *and* MARIE *enter right.*)

PEGGY. Girls, Marie and I have been talking over this affair about Red and we're afraid the boys are cheating us.

KATHLEEN. What makes you think that?

MARIE. For one thing, that terrible combination of diseases. It was too much—to develop over night.

KATHLEEN. That's right. I thought of that, too.

RUTH. But it might happen, don't you suppose? The boys seemed very sorry about it.

MARIE. Didn't you notice that the boys acted strangely when they told us about all this?

RUTH. I don't know. Did they?

PEGGY. Anyone could see that. I'll bet he's not sick. Red's too mean to be sick, anyway.

RUTH. Peggy, I think it's terrible for you to talk so, when the poor boy may be terribly sick.

KATHLEEN. He may be, Ruth, but probably he's well, and these rascal boys are playing some kind of a trick on us. We'd better find out abou' it and get our money back before they spend it.

FALSE PRETENSES

MARIE. That's exactly what I think. I don't trust those boys far.

PEGGY. We're going to walk down to Red's house this noon and ask his mother about it. We can get some lunch on the way. Come along, Kathleen, let's see what's at the bottom of this.

KATHLEEN. All right, I'll go. Coming, Ruth?—Frances?

(RUTH *and* FRANCES *shake heads,* PEGGY, MARIE, *and* KATHLEEN *exit back left.*)

FRANCES. Those girls would feel awful if they found a crêpe on the door, wouldn't they? Peggy would feel sorry for what she said about Red's being mean.

RUTH. Yes, she ought to. I thought it was terrible to say such a thing about him when he might have been dying at that very moment.

FRANCES. That's just what I thought of. (*Whispering.*) You know, they say that the ghost of a person just dead often comes to haunt those who talk about it.

RUTH. Wouldn't a red-headed ghost be awful? —Oh, Frances, don't let's talk about him any more. It makes me feel creepy.

FRANCES. Me too. I feel just dreadful about all this. Don't let's mention Red again. (RED, *who can be identified by his shock of hair, plods frowning across stage from right to left, not noticing girls. He selects a book and walks out. Girls cling to one another in fright.*) Oh—oh—it was Red.

RUTH. It must have been his ghost. He must have died.

FALSE PRETENSES

FRANCES. I knew something terrible would happen if we didn't stop talking.

RUTH. Oh, dear, what a sight. Come on, let's run.

(RUTH *and* FRANCES *run out right.* HARRY, SHORTY, *and* DAN *enter cautiously back from left.*)

HARRY (*entering first and looking around*). Those girls have gone now. Wow, I don't want to see any of them until we have the money to pay them back.

SHORTY. It's worse than not knowing a lesson to have to answer all their questions. That fool Jack nearly wrecked us with his ball and bat.

DAN. I have a hunch that we're going to get all tangled up before this thing is settled.

SHORTY. If Red will only stay away until next week, we can have things fixed up by that time.

(RED *walks in left.*)

DAN (*howling*). A-a-o-uh!

SHORTY. Oh! Where did you come from?

DAN. What business do you have . ? Don't you know you're sick?

HARRY (*aside*). Shut up, Dan; handle him easy. (*To* RED.) Thought you went to the fair, Red.

RED. I did start, but Uncle broke the rear axle on his car ten miles out of town, so we won't get to go on until to-morrow.

DAN. That's luck for you.

RED. It's the kind of bad luck I always have.

DAN. Listen, boy, your bad luck is nothing compared to ours.

[108]

RED. What's wrong with you? You didn't miss a trip to the fair.

DAN. No. But ——

HARRY (*breaking in suddenly*). Be still, Dan.— Red, I suppose you don't feel much like coming to school to-day?

RED. I'll say I don't. Think of it, missing a whole day at the fair, after I'd been counting on it.

HARRY. Red, why don't you play hookey? You'd be justified in doing it. I would if I were you.

RED. No. I'm not going to do that.

DAN. Why not?

RED. Because I'm not. What business is it of yours, anyway?

HARRY (*resolutely*). Red, you have to play hookey this afternoon. And you have to get out of here right now.

RED (*furiously*). Who says so?

SHORTY (*trying to look formidable*). We do.

RED. That makes me laugh.

DAN. Come on, Red, be reasonable.

RED. Be reasonable yourself. I don't want to go to school to-day but I'm not going to play hookey just because you tell me to. Suppose I'd get caught. Do you think I'd get to go to the fair to-morrow? I should say not.

HARRY. But you have to play hookey to-day, that's all there is to it.

DAN. Yes, and you'll have to act quick.

RED. Is that so? Make me if you can. (RED *sits down sullenly and tries to read.* HARRY, DAN, *and* SHORTY *exit back left after a brief whispered conference.* RUTH *and* FRANCES *walk in cautiously*

FALSE PRETENSES

at right, looking toward door at left where they last saw RED, *nearly stumble over* RED, *and after seeing him they run out right shrieking.* RED *gets up, looks out door where girls disappeared, and seats himself again and reads.* HARRY, DAN, *and* SHORTY *reappear back from left with a rope, creep forward stealthily, and suddenly loop* RED *to his chair.*) Hey! What are you trying to do?

HARRY (*knotting ropes*). If you won't play hookey, you are going to be kidnapped.

RED. Help! Help!

DAN. Shut up.

RED. I won't. I'll raise Cain until someone lets me loose and then I'll lick all three of you. Help! Help!

(SHORTY *muffles his last shout with a gag.* RED *is made fast to chair.*)

HARRY. We'll have to drag him to the closet until it is safe to let him loose.

DAN. Aye, aye, captain. Heave ho.

(*Boys tip chair on hind legs and pull it out left.* RUTH *and* FRANCES *peep in cautiously back from right.*)

FRANCES (*tiptoeing in*). I am sure it was his voice. Poor Red.

RUTH. Who would have thought a ghost could have such a loud voice?

FRANCES. He sounded as if he were in great pain, poor ghost.

RUTH. Yes, and angry, too, didn't he?

(SHORTY, DAN, *and* HARRY *enter left.*)

[110]

FALSE PRETENSES

FRANCES. Oh, boys, what is the latest news from Red? Is it true that—that —— (*A pause.*)

SHORTY. Girls, we hate to tell you the latest news from Red.

DAN. That's right, that's a fact. We do.

RUTH. Oh, we knew it! We knew it! We knew he was dead!

FRANCES. And—what do you think?—we saw his ghost—here—this noon—twice!

HARRY. His ghost! What?

RUTH. Yes, the first time it just walked slowly across the room ——

FRANCES. It picked up a book.

RUTH. Yes, it picked up a book, and disappeared.

DAN. Did Red—did he—did it say anything?

FRANCES. Not a word. It didn't seem to notice us at all.

HARRY. That's good. It's very unlucky to have a ghost speak to you.

SHORTY. But then you saw the ghost again?

RUTH. Yes, sitting in that chair—reading a paper. He looked so natural.

DAN. I'll bet he did.

HARRY (*adapting himself cautiously*). Girls, we didn't want to tell you the worst, but you have found it out. (*After a significant glance at his colleagues.*) Poor Red is no more!

SHORTY (*following lead*). No, alas, the diseased has departed.

FRANCES. Isn't it terrible?

DAN. That's right. That's a fact. It surely is!

FALSE PRETENSES

(JACK *and* BILL *enter back from left with some packages, obviously sporting goods, which they place on table.*)

BILL (*cheerfully*).   We sent the flowers, folks, and I suppose they will help Red recover quickly.

JACK.   Yes, he'll be with us next week, no doubt.

RUTH.   What?   Haven't you heard the dreadful news?

JACK.   No.   What is it?

RUTH *and* FRANCES (*in tragic unison*).   He's dead!

BILL *and* JACK.   What?   Who?   Red?

(*Girls nod.* BILL *and* JACK *turn to other boys, who nod solemnly.*)

FRANCES.   Ruth, let's go to our room.

(*Girls leave stage right.*)

BILL.   Look here, you fellows, what kind of a frame-up is this?   Why are you trying to improve on the scheme?

JACK.   You had no right to let him die without consulting us.

HARRY.   It was a sad necessity.

JACK.   How's that?

HARRY.   Those girls saw his ghost, here.   If they see his ghost doesn't that make it necessary for him to be dead?

BILL.   Aw!   What do you mean, ghost?

SHORTY.   We mean Red didn't go away.   He came back.

JACK.   I had a hunch that fellow couldn't be trusted.

FALSE PRETENSES

HARRY. We don't have to trust him now. Don't think we haven't been on the job while you were gone. We have him, bound and gagged in the next room, because he won't play hookey.

JACK. And the girls saw him and think he is a ghost?

DAN. That's it.

BILL. Wow, what a close shave! Let's have a look at the prisoner.

DAN. We better tighten that gag while we're looking. If he gets his mouth free, he'll raise the roof.

(*Boys go out left.* PEGGY, MARIE, *and* KATH-LEEN *enter back from left.*)

PEGGY (*tearing wrappings from packages on table*). Here's the stuff. Oh, those rascals!

KATHLEEN. I wonder where the other girls are. Won't they be wild when they hear about it?

PEGGY. They thought the boys were all right. This will show them.

MARIE. Get this stuff together, Peggy, and I'll take it back.

(RUTH *and* FRANCES *enter right.*)

FRANCES. I suppose you've heard the dreadful news?

KATHLEEN. We've heard some dreadful news all right, but how did you get hold of it?

FRANCES. Girls, would you believe it, a few minutes after he died we saw his ghost, here in this room.

MARIE. Ghost? Whose ghost?

FALSE PRETENSES

RUTH. Whose do you suppose? Poor Red's.

PEGGY. Ghost nothing. Who says he is dead?

RUTH. The boys all said so.

MARIE. Yes, I suppose they would. They may say anything.

PEGGY. Girls, if Red is dead, his mother doesn't know anything about it. He hasn't been sick at all. He was out of town this morning, and she saw him start to school this afternoon.

FRANCES. But the boys said ——

KATHLEEN. Don't you believe a word they said. That was all a scheme to get our money, just as we suspected.

RUTH. A scheme? Do you mean they lied to us?

KATHLEEN. Yes. It's a tangled story. We went to Red's house and found that this morning he started to the state fair, but returned unexpectedly and started for school this afternoon. Then as we returned through town we saw Bill and Jack coming out of a sporting goods store with a lot of packages. We waited until they had turned the corner and then we asked some questions in the store. The manager said the boys had bought over five dollars' worth of sporting goods which were on sale. That's what they were collecting the money for, I suppose.

RUTH. Oh, the mean things!

FRANCES. Now how will we get our money back?

PEGGY. I fixed that up. I told the salesman about the trick the boys had played on us, and he said if we could get possession of the goods he would refund us the money.

MARIE. And we have the stuff. The boys carelessly left it here in this room. So we're sure of our money.

FRANCES. You girls have surely been clever about it. Let's take it right back and get the money.

KATHLEEN. Marie is going to take it herself.

RUTH. Why can't we all go with her?

PEGGY. We have a better scheme than that. Let Marie take it by herself, and the rest of us will stay here and make life miserable for those boys.

RUTH. Wait until I get the chance; I'll tell them something they won't soon forget.

PEGGY. No, you mustn't accuse them. Act as though you believe their story that Red is dead, and see how soon they'll get tangled up in their own lies.

KATHLEEN. Or else see their faces when Red walks in to school this afternoon.

RUTH. But he must be here now. That wasn't his ghost, it was Red.

KATHLEEN. Oh, girls, this will be worth seeing.

MARIE. While you're seeing it through here, I'll go get the money.

PEGGY. Marie, if you find there's anything left over, buy us something nice.

MARIE. Leave that to me. [*Exit back to left.*

RUTH. My, I'm so bewildered I can't think straight.

PEGGY. I wonder if the boys know Red is here? They'll be busy trying to keep him away from us if they do.

FRANCES. Did you ever hear of such a wicked scheme? I can't get over it.

KATHLEEN. Don't worry about that now. Our

money is safe, and it's going to be worth all our excitement and misspent sympathy to see those boys caught in their own snares.

RUTH. What shall we say to them?

KATHLEEN. Leave that to the inspiration of the moment. They are the ones who will have to do the worrying.

(SHORTY, DAN, *and* HARRY *enter left, hesitate as they see girls.*)

PEGGY. Oh, boys, isn't it terrible about poor Red?

DAN. Yes, it's awful, that's a fact. (*Aside to* SHORTY.) She'd think so if she saw him tied to that chair.

SHORTY. Shh!

KATHLEEN. Was there an operation,—Shorty? We heard there was one.

SHORTY (*seeing* HARRY *nod*). Why, yes. Early this morning they—cut off both his feet.

FRANCES. Oh, how sad.

PEGGY. But someone said he saw Red out with his uncle in his automobile this morning. Was that possible,—Dan?

DAN. Um—yes, the doctors—thought a ride in the fresh air might do him some good.

RUTH. Poor boy. When will they have the funeral?

HARRY. Friday, at two o'clock.

PEGGY. I suppose all of us ought to go. (JACK *and* BILL *enter left.*) We were just talking about going to Red's funeral. I suppose you know when it is to be held, Bill?

FALSE PRETENSES

BILL (*failing to see* HARRY's *signal*). Yes, next Saturday morning.

KATHLEEN. But, Harry, didn't you say it would be Friday afternoon?

HARRY. Yes, I did, but I suppose they changed it—on account of—on account of the ball game, maybe.

BILL. Yes, that's right, they changed it on account of the ball game.

PEGGY. Did Red suffer much pain' before he died?—Jack?

JACK. Yes, he did.—Just before he died, he had the most terrible pains.

FRANCES. Where, Jack?

JACK. In his—in his feet.

RUTH. Why, Jack, didn't you know that they cut off both his feet? Shorty told us that.

JACK. They did? (*Girls and boys nod.*) That's right, they did. I forgot that. His feet weren't really there, but he thought they were,—and that's where he thought the pain was.

KATHLEEN. But why did they cut off his feet, Shorty?

SHORTY. Well,—because,—because they were afraid of ptomaine poisoning.

(*Girls shriek with laughter, boys look dismayed.*)

PEGGY. Forgive us, boys, but this awful strain has made us hysterical.

DAN. It's going to make me hysterical in a minute.

PEGGY. You'll agree with us that it's an awful strain, won't you, Bill?

FALSE PRETENSES

BILL. I'll agree with anything you say if you don't put it in the form of a question.

RED'S VOICE (*muffled, outside left*). Oh, my feet, my feet, my feet!

KATHLEEN (*aside to girls*). Girls, they have Red locked up somewhere.

DAN (*aside to boys*). I told you that gag wouldn't hold.

RUTH (*aside to girls*). Let's pretend we think it's a ghost. (*To boys.*) There, that's the ghost again. We heard it before, didn't we, Frances?

FRANCES. Yes, the very same voice. Poor thing. He's worrying about his feet. I suppose he's just found out they cut them off.

RUTH. But, Harry, the ghost had feet when we saw him. Didn't he, Frances?

RED'S VOICE. Oh, it's cutting my feet. Help. Help.

HARRY (*desperately*). That's a ghost, all right. Aren't you girls afraid? Don't you think you had better go?

KATHLEEN. No, we're not afraid. Are you?

HARRY. Certainly not. But if I were you I would get out of here. Better go right away. We fellows will watch for the ghost and ——

RED'S VOICE (*no longer muffled*). Help. The ropes are cutting my feet. Let me loose.

PEGGY. The poor ghost. Let's go see what is wrong with him. (*Girls start toward door.*)

DAN (*desperately*). Now, girls, I wouldn't go in there. It isn't safe. You don't know what a ghost might do.

PEGGY. I'm going and I'm going by myself.

You boys stay right here and take care of the girls. [*Goes out left.*

SHORTY (*moving toward back*). I just remembered some work I ought to do ——

BILL. Yes, I ought to be going too ——

(*Boys start out back and right.*)

KATHLEEN (*intercepting*). Here, no you don't. Don't run off and leave us, you cowards.

(*As the boys are turned back into room,* RED *enters left, followed by* PEGGY, *holding ropes.*)

RED. You big cowards, if you'll come outside after school I'll lick all of you. Girls, they've had me tied up for half an hour. I ——

RUTH. We know all about it. Do you know why they did it?

RED. No. Do you?

RUTH. Yes. They told us you were sick to get our money for flowers and then they spent the money for baseball supplies. Naturally they didn't want you to be seen.

RED. Then that's why they tried to make me play hookey?

PEGGY. It must have been.—Oh, you mean, dishonest boys, for half a cent I'd call the police.

HARRY. Don't do that. Give us a chance. We'll explain it all.

BILL. We meant to pay you back, honest we did.

FRANCES. Yes, you would have to pay us back when we found out.

FALSE PRETENSES

DAN. We'll take the stuff back and get your money for you right away.

RUTH. You don't have to do that. We've found the stuff and sent it back (*As* MARIE *comes in back.*) and here's Marie. With the money, Marie?

MARIE. Yes, indeed. And with a surprise. But did the bold, bad story-tellers finally disagree?

FRANCES. They surely did. Sorry you missed that part of the fun.

MARIE. Let's get settled. I don't want to carry all this money. Peggy, here's your seventy-five cents; Kathleen, here's your fifty cents; Ruth, here's seventy-five cents; Frances, one dollar; and that leaves my dollar for me. So it's all settled.

SHORTY (*watching intently*). But—but wasn't there any more money?

MARIE. Yes, that's where the surprise comes in. Strange to say, there was $1.72 left.

DAN (*fervently*). Our money!

MARIE (*ignoring* DAN). Not knowing what else to do with it, I bought five cute little boxes of candy, at thirty-five cents each, just one for each (*She pauses; boys look expectant.*) of us girls, and here you are. (*Distributes to girls.*)

KATHLEEN. Oh, Marie, you have the best ideas. I think that was a good way to settle it.

JACK (*aggressively*). But, look here, that $1.72 was our money.

PEGGY. Now, Jack, no freshness from you. If you don't like the way Marie has settled this matter, would you rather take it up with the teachers, or, our parents?

JACK (*beaten*). No, I guess not. But ——

FALSE PRETENSES

PEGGY. Then, in the words of your famous resolutions, " Amen, so be it." (*Turns.*) Have a piece of candy, Red.

RED. Thanks, yes.

FRANCES. Take some of mine, too.

(*Girls crowd around* RED, *offering him candy, and so they exit right.*)

SHORTY (*pointing to* HARRY). And so this is your scheme! You are the one who claimed to have thought out this plan!

HARRY. You're the one who said: " As for the scheme, we all thought up that."

BILL. And Jack, blurting out ball and bat, that's what gave it away.

DAN. Oh, don't let's row any more about this. There's no use trying to pick out the prize fool in this crowd; we're all too close to first place.

JACK. The prize for fool is about all we have left, now. We've lost everything else.

HARRY (*moodily*). Our money—that's lost.

BILL. And our sporting goods ——

DAN. And our reputations ——

SHORTY (*cheerfully*). Still, we have something left.

JACK. What, I'd like to know?

SHORTY (*proudly drawing paper from pocket*). The resolutions!

BILL. Bah!

(HARRY *snatches the paper from* SHORTY'S *hands, and is viciously tearing it to bits, on which the others are stamping, as the curtain goes down.*)

[121]

THE ESTABROOK NIECES

"The Estabrook Nieces" was first produced at Dennis Junior High School, Richmond, Indiana, in November, 1923, with the following cast:

Dud	Ellis Bevington
Sam	Finley Bond
Charley	Jacob Worley
Ted	Harold Green
Edith	Elizabeth Kreimeier
Lucille	Lucille Harris
Barbara	Marie Mackey
Mary	Thelma May

THE ESTABROOK NIECES

SCENE:—*The living-room of a typical American home; the time is a summer evening. To the right, set in a diagonal wall, is a series of panelled windows, one of which is open to the darkness outside. Against the rear wall, in the center, is a grand piano, on which are shaded lights. At the front right is a small table bearing a telephone and a shaded light. A large davenport is in the center of the room, in front of the piano. At the left, near the front, is a library table covered with books, and near it a floor lamp and a large chair with a high back. There is a doorway from the left behind this table and chair. The other entrances are at the front of the stage, right and left.*

(*As the curtain rises there is no person on the stage, but outside is heard the sound of talking and laughter. Dud appears cautiously at the open window. After a careful survey of the room, he climbs in, looks about, peers out the left entrance to the rear, and then returns to the window and gives a low whistle. An answering whistle is heard; then* Charley *and* Sam *appear at the window and come in.*)

Sam. Is the coast clear?

Dud. Yes, they're all in the next room, and making so much noise they'll never notice us.

Charley. Suppose they drift this way?

[125]

DUD. Plenty of places about here to hide, aren't there? Better pick yourself a place now if you feel nervous.

SAM. It's five after nine. When was Ted to meet us here?

DUD. Nine o'clock was the hour he set in his note. He's held up somewhere or he'd be here now.

CHARLEY. I don't feel easy. Whatever we're going to do, let's do it and make a getaway. That party crowd may rush in on us any minute.

SAM. Keep your nerve, Charley. You're not in any danger as long as you are carrying out instructions.

CHARLEY. Maybe we got in the wrong room. What did the note say?

DUD. "Living-room window on north side of house." We couldn't make a mistake on that. Quiet down, Charley, and quit your fretting. You'll live through this.

SAM (*looking out rear left*). Under cover, gang. They're coming in here.

(SAM *and* DUD *hide under the piano, over which a long scarf is hanging.* CHARLEY *looks about in frantic terror and finally hustles out the window.* EDITH, LUCILLE, BARBARA, *and* MARY *enter rear left.*)

EDITH (*going to piano*). I have the music right here, Barbara. I know the girls would love to hear you sing it.

LUCILLE. Yes, do sing it. I've never heard the song, and I want to lear it.

THE ESTABROOK NIECES

BARBARA. But I don't know it very well, girls.

MARY. At least you know it better than we do.

BARBARA. All right, then. If I am to sing, I'd rather do it before the other guests arrive. I don't mind my chums for an audience, but strange girls, especially when one of them is a wonderful singer, make me a bit—oh, short of breath—you know the feeling.

EDITH (*amused*). Then sing it, Barbara, while you have the breath left.

MARY. Barbara, if I could sing at all, I'd never feel short of breath for anyone.

BARBARA. Oh, yes you would, if you had to sing before Dolores—what's her name, Edith?

EDITH. Campbell—Dolores Campbell.

BARBARA. Have any of you girls met her yet? (*Shaking of heads.*) They say she has studied voice in New York.

(*The telephone rings;* EDITH *answers.*)

EDITH. Yes—this is Edith, Mrs. Estabrook. . . . Yes. (*Long pause.*) Oh, I'm so sorry— I hope it won't be serious. . . . Yes, indeed. . . . Thank you. . . . Good-bye. (*Hangs receiver.*) Barbara, you won't have to lose your breath to-night. Dolores Campbell isn't coming.

MARY. Not coming? Couldn't she have let you know sooner?

LUCILLE. I should think so. It's after nine o'clock.

EDITH. She had been expecting to come, but her cousin Helena Campbell, who was coming with her, has a sore throat, and became so ill while she was dressing that they won't be able to come.

Lucille. How about Clarice Estabrook? She's coming, isn't she? She's the one I really want to meet.

Edith. She's not coming, either. You know, it all seems rather strange to me. Mrs. Estabrook says that Helena isn't seriously ill at all, but that Clarice and Dolores insist on remaining with her. She said, "You know how devoted they are to one another."

Mary. Who are these devoted damsels? Are they sisters?

Edith. No, they are cousins, and nieces of old Mrs. Estabrook. She is very fond of them, and has them visit her every year at her summer home, so they are more like sisters than cousins.

Lucille. Where did you meet them, Edith?

Edith. I haven't met them. Mother asked them because Mrs. Estabrook wants them to meet some girls of their age.

Barbara. I'm really very sorry they're not coming.

Mary. Even at the risk of losing your breath?

Barbara. Yes. I have heard they are very interesting.

Edith (*going to rear left*). Come along, all of you, and help me tell Mother that the party has dwindled to four. This makes it much more cozy and informal.

Lucille. Yes, now Barbara can sing the rest of the evening, and not lose her breath at all.

THE ESTABROOK NIECES

(*Girls go out rear left.* SAM *and* DUD *emerge from hiding.*)

DUD. What happened to Charley?

SAM. He went out the window. Probably got cold feet and ran home.

CHARLEY (*head appearing in window*). No, I didn't. I've been here all the time.

SAM. Come on in, Charley, and be still.

(CHARLEY *enters.*)

CHARLEY. Why doesn't Ted show up?

SAM. Steady, Charley. Remember, he couldn't get to us while those girls were here.

CHARLEY. We'll get caught sure if we don't get out of the house soon.

(*The three boys have gathered in front center of stage.* TED *enters stealthily from rear left, unnoticed.*)

DUD. I'm beginning to wonder myself what Ted meant by getting us into a place like this. A party of girls running through the house. He ought to know we'll get caught sooner or later if we hang around too long.

TED (*yelling*). *Say!* How are you, fellows? (*Laughs at their start.*)

DUD. Oh, fine.

CHARLEY (*who has collapsed into a chair*). I'll be all right in a minute, when my heart gets down out of my neck.

SAM. Where have you been, Ted? Tell us what's up?

DUD. Yes, what's on for to-night? Lead us to it.

TED. Sit down, boys. Make yourselves at home.

SAM. What will your folks say if they catch us here?

TED. What can they say? I think I've a right to entertain my friends in one room of the house, if Sis can have girls running wild all over the rest of it.

DUD. Charley nearly had a chill, waiting for you to come.

CHARLEY. I'm beginning to feel at home now, but I don't like to go crawling in other people's windows at night. It looks bad.

TED. What do you care how it looks if I give you a written invitation to do it? (*Finding box on table.*) Here, Charley, steady your nerves on this candy. (*Passes candy; they eat.*)

DUD. Well, Ted, what's up? Why the most mysterious summons to come snooping in your windows at nine o'clock?

TED. My boys, the reason is—eats.

SAM. Eats? Aha, very thoughtful of you, Ted.

TED. Wait a minute. I'm sorry, I should have said " The reason was eats." Half an hour ago the prospect was bright for you all to be fed on three kinds of sandwiches, salad, olives, ice-cream and cake. Now the prospect is black—in fact, it's a lost hope.

DUD. And you brought us here to tell us this?

TED. It all happened since I sent for you, Dud.

CHARLEY. What happened?

THE ESTABROOK NIECES

TED. I lost my job as butler. You see, Sis has this birthday party and Mother had invited three young swells, the nieces of old Mrs. Estabrook.

SAM. Sure. Clarice, Dolores, and Helena, to be explicit.

TED. Where did you get that, Sam?

SAM. Lying under the piano, I heard your sister receive the sad news that because of Helena's sore throat, the three devoted cousins can't come.

TED. That's how I lost my job as butler. To carry out a few fancy ideas of Mother's, I was to lug the grub to the distinguished guests. I sent for you, intending to slip three plates out the window.— By the way, if you'll read that note again, you'll find it says " Come to the window." Not through it.

CHARLEY. Yaah. I knew there was something wrong.

DUD. Shut up, Charley. Well, Ted, what about it now?

TED. Now that the party is reduced to Sis and her three chums, Mother says I don't need to be the butler. So that's where you lost out on the lunch.

DUD. Why don't you tell your mother that you want to serve the lunch anyway?

TED. Ho! Ho! I'd never get away with that, after I've been growling all day about having to do it. And besides, while I might get her to lose count on seven plates and serve three extra, I'd never be able to do it with only four to serve. You fellows are out of luck, that's all. Better fill up on the chocolates; that's all you'll get.

SAM. What luck!

Dud. Pretty rotten, isn't it?

Charley. And if we were only girls, we'd get all that stuff to eat.

Ted. Eh? (*He gazes ahead thoughtfully; as the others watch him his face broadens into a grin*). Oh, Charley, what an idea to put into my head! If we were only girls. There's the solution. Be girls! Be Clarice, Dolores, and Helena!

Dud. I see, Ted. Dress up, eh?

Ted. Sure. You and Sam have sisters about your size. Borrow your outfits from them, and between you you can fit up Charley. Up-stairs I have those three wigs we used at the masquerade. What more do we need?

Sam. That part's all right. But these girls have never seen the devoted trio, Clarice, Dolores, and Helena?

Dud. Surely not. Don't you remember what we overheard them say?

Sam. We're all set, then. Oh, boy, what a wonderful idea!

Dud. It's slick, I'll say.

Sam. But we'll have to 'phone in and reverse the regrets—tell 'em the sick girl recovered and we're on our way to the party, won't we?

Ted. Yep. You do that, will you, Sam?

Sam. Sure. Come on, let's go, or it will be too late.

Charley (*as others move to front left*). But I don't understand.

Dud. Of course not. Just follow orders, though. You'll get fed to-night, and to-morrow we'll explain to you how it happened.

THE ESTABROOK NIECES

TED. Hurry! The girls are coming in here. I'll let you out the side door and get you the wigs.

(*Boys exit front left. Girls enter back left a moment later.*)

LUCILLE. Barbara, you must sing us that song now. We won't be put off any longer.

BARBARA. All right, if only to stop your begging, I'll do it.

EDITH. Here's the music. Will you play it, Mary?

MARY. I'll try it if Barbara is willing.

BARBARA. Delighted. Here's the music.

(BARBARA *sings.*)

LUCILLE. Beautiful. Oh, Barbara, that was lovely.

BARBARA. Thank you.

EDITH. Yes, it was charming. And the accompaniment was splendid, Mary. (*Telephone rings,* TED *slips in unobtrusively at front left and sits with a book.*) Excuse me a moment, girls. (*At 'phone.*) Yes. . . Who? . . . Oh, this is Helena Campbell. . . . Yes, I'm delighted to hear it. . . . That's very good of you. . . . Yes, come right along; the other girls are eager to meet you and your cousins. . . . Yes, that's the address. . . . Good-bye. (*Hangs receiver.*) Oh, girls, did you ever hear anything so strange? That was Helena Campbell. She said that her throat was suddenly so much better, and that she regretted so much keeping her cousins Clarice and Dolores from the party, that she had decided to come and bring them along, since they would not come without her.

MARY. Can you imagine anything like that? Coming at this hour, and to a stranger's house.

LUCILLE. Sounds a bit strange, doesn't it? What queer persons they must be.

MARY. I wonder if they made up that excuse in the first place and later decided they wanted to come after all?

EDITH. No, it was old Mrs. Estabrook who called first, you remember, and I have no doubt Helena has sore throat. She sounded as hoarse as a frog.

BARBARA. Shouldn't we tell your mother about it? She's not expecting them, is she?

EDITH. Not now. Poor mother, she won't know what to expect next. Let's go tell her

(*Girls go out back left.* DUD, *in a wig and feminine garb, appears at the window.*)

DUD. Yoo, hoo! (*Leaps in window with masculine agility.*)

TED. Oh, Dud, how unladylike, to come in the window! What would Mrs. Estabrook say? What would your cousins think?

DUD. How do you like me? I think I'm sweet.

TED (*aiming a blow at him*). You darling!

DUD. Hey. Look out! I can't fight in these clothes or they'll all come off. Every time I draw a deep breath something goes " ping " behind.

TED (*investigating*). You've drawn several, then; you're about pinged loose.

Dud. Fix me up, will you? I called instead of Sam.

Ted. Yes, I was right here and heard Sis answer. She told the girls that poor Helena sounded as hoarse as a frog.

Dud. What's loose back there?

Ted. There are two buttons gone entirely. I'll have to pin it.

Dud. Better sew me in with needle and thread. (Ted *sticks*.) Oww!

Ted. Say, Claribel, don't be so noisy. We don't want the girls to come flocking in and see you now.

Dud. Be careful yourself. I'd rather lose the dress than have it pinned to me.

(Sam *and* Charley, *wigged and dressed in girls' clothes, appear at the open window.* Charley *is garbed in a raincoat.*)

Sam. What a pretty scene! Come on, Charley my girl.

(*They come through the window, and the boys examine each other with ill-suppressed shrieks.*)

Ted. Be quiet, fellows. Let's get organized and then you'll have to make your grand entrance at the door. They'll serve the lunch at ten o'clock, so you ought to be getting in.

Sam. Oh, but you must see Charley; she is a jewel. Unswath yourself, Charley, the storm is over.

Charley. I'm cold. I'm freezing now. I'm not used to wearing these clothes.

Sam. Really?

Dud. You'll have to come out of your shell or

you'll get no eats to-night. You don't suppose a niece of old Mrs. Estabrook would come to a party wrapped up like that? Why, you look like—like a member of the volunteer fire department.

CHARLEY. If it weren't for the eats I'd never go through all this nutty business.

SAM. Well, what do you suppose the rest of us are doing this for, fun? Come on, come out of it.

DUD (*seeing* CHARLEY's *neck*). Oho! Ho! Ho! (CHARLEY *puts hands to back and whirls to keep himself from ridicule.*) Look here! (*Captures* CHARLEY *and turns him around, revealing a broad dark streak around his neck.*) Isn't he the dainty milk-fed creature?

SAM. Reminds me of that poem we learned about " The Shades of Night Were Falling Fast "—some of 'em fell on Charley.

DUD (*rubbing* CHARLEY's *neck vigorously*). They fell fast, too. Won't come off.—Get some flour, Ted.

TED. What for?

DUD. Camouflage. Think of the scandal that would be created if an Estabrook niece went to a party looking like that.

(TED *goes out front left hurriedly.*)

CHARLEY. What's the matter with me anyway? I think I look as good as any of you.

SAM. Charley, I hate to tell you, but—your neck isn't the right shade at all, for a society lady.

CHARLEY. That's just tan.

DUD. Yes, black and tan.

(TED *reënters with cup of flour.*)

[136]

THE ESTABROOK NIECES

TED. Here, Charley. We'll make you a delicate pale person now.

(*They brush flour on* CHARLEY *and others.*)

CHARLEY. Put on lots. Maybe it will help me keep warm.

TED. Here, Dud, you need some too.

CHARLEY. Yah, Dud, I guess I'm no worse than you are.

DUD. I'm five shades lighter at least. Come on, now, let's go.

TED. But have you decided who you are? Which is which?

SAM. I'll be Dolores—Charley, you be Clarice, and Dud, you'll be—what's her name ——?

DUD. Helena. She's the one with the sore throat. Say, oughtn't I have my neck wrapped up?

SAM. Sure. Where's a handkerchief?

CHARLEY (*pausing in a futile effort*). I couldn't get mine if I had to.

TED. Here's one. (*Ties up* DUD.) Hurry now, get outside and ring the bell.

(*The three boys go out the window.* TED *returns to chair front left and sits restlessly until door-bell rings. Girls run in left.*)

MARY. It must be the Estabrook nieces.

BARBARA. How exciting!

(*The girls seat themselves.* EDITH *goes to front door right, and reënters with the "nieces."*)

EDITH. I'm so glad you were able to come. (*To* DUD.) I suppose this is Helena. (DUD *nods.*)

I hope your throat will not give you any more
trouble. (*An awkward pause.*) But you must in-
troduce yourselves. I'm Edith McKensie, and these
are my friends, Lucille, Barbara, and Mary—and
my brother Ted.

Dud. I'm Helena, as you guessed. I suppose
you noticed the bandage.—But my throat's much
better.

Barbara. You must be careful, though, Helena.
Your voice still sounds very hoarse.

(Lucille *greets* Dud, *and they sit on davenport
in center stage.*)

Edith (*to* Sam). And you are ———?

Sam (*loudly*). I'm Dolores. (*Joins* Dud *on
davenport.*)

Mary (*to* Barbara). A singer, with a voice like
that?

Barbara (*aside*). Maybe she has a cold too.
(*Going over to* Sam.) Dolores, have you a cold
too?

Sam. Me? I should say not. (*Slapping chest
until* Dud *restrains him.*) I'm never sick.

Edith (*to* Charley). And your name is ———?

Charley (*bewildered*). My name is—is ———

Edith. Surely, you must be Clarice.

Charley (*in relief*). Yes, I must be. There is
nothing else left for me to be, is there?

Mary. Oh, Clarice, how funny you are.

Edith. Won't you all be seated? (*They sit
awkwardly; there is a moment of nervous silence.*)
It was so good of you to come, in spite of your
difficulties.

Dud. Yes, but we can't stay long. (*Meaningly.*) Until ten, or a few minutes after.

Mary. Dolores, we have heard so much about your studying in New York. Can't you tell us of your experiences?

Sam. Who, me?

Lucille. Yes, do tell us about your teachers.

Sam. Which ones?

Lucille. Your New York voice teachers.

Sam. Well—(*Haltingly.*) the first one I had taught me to—to—sing dol-re-mi-fal-sol—and—and—but, say, you don't want to hear about all that. It would be an awful bore to you.

Barbara. Don't tell us about that, then. I'd much rather hear you sing. Won't you please sing something now?

Lucille. Oh, do, please.

Sam. Impossible!—You see, I left all my music in New York.

Edith. But I have lots of music here. I'm sure you would know some of it.

(Edith *goes to piano;* Lucille *joins her in looking through music.*)

Sam. Probably not. I sing only special kinds of music.

Mary. We'd be glad to hear you sing anything, even the simplest song.

(Ted *joins* Dud *on the davenport.*)

Barbara. Ted, can't you help us to persuade Dolores to sing for us?

TED. Go ahead and sing, Dolores. (*Aside to* DUD.) I can stand it if the rest of them can.

EDITH (*at piano*). Come over here and pick out a song, won't you, Dolores?

SAM (*advancing unwillingly*). I'd rather not, but since it seems to be expected of me, I suppose I'll have to.

DUD (*to* TED). Seems I felt something go " ping." Look me over, will you?

TED. You're all together.

EDITH (*turning through music*). Do you see anything here you know?

SAM. Never saw any of it before. Don't you have a regular song book?

CHARLEY (*coming over, whispering*). Ted! What's my name?

TED. Clarice. Don't forget it, now.

CHARLEY. Clarice. Clarice. I just can't remember that. (*Returns to right stage.*)

EDITH (*striking chord*). Dolores will sing " The Last Rose of Summer."

MARY. Oh, how nice.

(SAM *sings, but not in time or tune. The girls cover their astonishment and applaud politely.* SAM *attempts a profound bow, and his wig falls to the floor.*)

EDITH. Sam! What are you up to?

SAM (*addressing wig*). Well, if you had to fall off, why didn't you fall before I had to sing!

(TED *slips quietly out front left.*)

[140]

Dud. I wish it had fallen off. That hurt us worse than it did you.

Lucille. Are you really Helena? I'll bet you're not. (*She snatches off* Dud's *wig.*)

Edith. Dud! You too?

Dud. Don't expose me.—Think of my sore throat.

Mary (*grabbing* Charley *by the foot as he starts out window*). Hey, help me hold this one.— What is your name?

Charley. Eh? Oh, Clarice. You can't fool me. I know it this time.

Mary (*pulling off his wig*). Aha. Another deceiver uncovered. (*To* Barbara.) Only Charley. No wonder he didn't know his name.

Edith. Ted!—Where is that fellow? He put you up to this, didn't he, Sam?

Sam. That's hardly the way to say it. We didn't want you to be disappointed by the absence of your guests.

Edith. That's right. Stick up for Ted. I know he's the rascal at the bottom of this. It looks like some of his work.

Barbara. But what ever made you do it? Did you enjoy it?

Dud. Did we enjoy it? I should say not.

Barbara. Then if it was so unpleasant, why do it? We didn't beg you, you know.

Mary. Yes, and don't think we'll believe that you did this for our benefit.

Dud. We were carrying out a little plan of our own.

Edith. Barbara, when you've had a brother's

gang hanging around your parties as long as I have, you'll know what one great desire constantly animates them.—Charley, tell the girls what you were after.

CHARLEY. I was after Sam. I came in last.

EDITH. You know what I mean. You were after the refreshments, weren't you?

CHARLEY. I guess so.

LUCILLE. I see now. They must have been hungry to have gone to all that trouble.

EDITH. It isn't hunger, it's the fear of being left out and the desire to put one over on us. They used to steal the refreshments. Notice how refined and subtle their methods have become.

SAM. The method wasn't so bad at that. We were all going along in good shape until my wig fell off.

MARY. Your singing must have jarred it loose.

LUCILLE. Sam, I never had such a struggle to keep from shrieking out as I did during your solo.

EDITH. Nor I either. I know I hit a lot of wrong notes, because I was laughing so.

SAM. So that was it? I thought it didn't sound just right.

EDITH. Well, Dolores, your singing has earned you your supper.

SAM. What about the others?

EDITH. We'll feed Clarice and Helena for good measure.

SAM. Well, I wouldn't feel comfortable unless they are fed too. " You know how devoted we are to one another."

THE ESTABROOK NIECES

(TED *enters front left with two plates, presents to* LUCILLE *and* BARBARA *with the comment* "*Allow me.*")

EDITH. Ted! Come here.

TED (*sweetly*). In just a moment, sister. I'm very busy now.   [*Exits.*

MARY. He seems restless, doesn't he?

EDITH. He knows what's coming. I wonder how he'll get out of it this time. (TED *reappears and serves* MARY *and* EDITH.) Ted, I want to know ——

TED. Now, in just a minute, sister, as soon as I've finished —— (*Goes out again.*)

EDITH. When he says " sister," then I know I've got him thinking. I wonder what he'll say about all this.

DUD. You had better be deciding what you'll say.

EDITH. Oh, he talks you out of things too, does he?

SAM. When he opens his mouth to argue, we give up.

(TED *reappears with four plates, serves boys and sets one down.*)

TED (*serving* SAM). Bird seed for the canary.

EDITH. Ted, come here at once. I have something to say to you.

TED (*going out door*). May I serve the ice-cream first?   [*Exits.*

BARBARA (*laughing*). He's slippery as an eel, isn't he? You ought to forgive him, Edith.

[143]

EDITH. Forgive him? I've done that long ago. I'm merely eager to hear what kind of an explanation he'll put up. It will certainly be good. You don't know Ted as well as I do.

TED (*dashing in*). Someone has stolen the ice-cream. I left the freezer on the back porch, all opened and ready to serve, and when I went back to get it, it was gone.

DUD. Up and at 'em, gang. We'll catch the thieves.

SAM. Yea. They can't be far away.

(*Boys swarm out two left entrances and window.*)

MARY. Let's see what's going on.

LUCILLE. Let's join in the chase. Oh, isn't this exciting! (MARY *and* LUCILLE *start out left.*)

EDITH. Come on, we can go out the front door.
[*Exit from right.*

BARBARA (*calling after them*). I'll stay here and see that the plates aren't stolen.

(*She crosses stage and sits in high-backed chair under floor lamp. There are confused sounds of running and shouting outside. TED enters stealthily rear left, thinks room empty, goes to window, whistles;* SAM *answers and appears;* BARBARA *listens intently.*)

TED. Sam, the ice-cream is under those bushes next to the garage.

SAM. Who put it there?

TED. I did. I didn't know whether Edith was angry, so I thought we'd stage a mock rescue of the ice-cream, and make ourselves popular.

[144]

SAM. Good enough idea. But the girls are on the hunt now. They're all over the yard.

TED. Watch your chance. Get the freezer when you can, and then come back and tell a tale about how you took it away from three or four thugs. Anything to get Sis off my trail.

SAM. All righto. I'll do my best.

(SAM *disappears.* TED *exits rear left.*)

BARBARA (*calling out window*). Edith. Edith.

EDITH (*outside*). Yoo hoo. Coming. (*Appears at window.*) What's the matter now? Has someone stolen the plates too?

(MARY *joins* EDITH *at the window.*)

BARBARA. No, but Ted has hidden the ice-cream in the bushes next to the garage so that Sam can bring it in with a faked story of how he took it away from three or four thugs, and it's all so that you'll forget to scold Ted for letting the boys in.

MARY. How do you know that, Barbara?

BARBARA. I heard Ted himself talking out this window to Sam about it.

EDITH. Oh, but he thinks he's clever, doesn't he?

MARY. Let's get the ice-cream ourselves, Edith.

EDITH. We'll do that, and then let him explain both his tricks. I think he's fairly caught this time.

(*They disappear.*)

LUCILLE (*coming in front right*). Where are the girls going now?

BARBARA. After the ice-cream. Ted hid it himself so that he and the boys could feature a daring rescue of the refreshments and get themselves forgiven for their masquerading.

Lucille. Well, aren't brothers a blessing? I never knew one as bad as Ted, though. You can't keep up with his tricks.

Barbara. That fellow is a terror, surely.

(Edith *and* Mary *enter front right with the freezer.*)

Edith. There we are. Did you hear about this last stunt, Lucille?

Lucille. Barbara has just been telling me.

Edith. We've caught them fairly this time. (*Calling out window.*) Ted! Sam!—Come on in, we've got the ice-cream. (*Aside to girls.*) We've got you too.

Mary. Are you going to feed them now, after the way they've acted?

Edith. I might as well. They'll be quiet and out of mischief while they are eating, at least.

Lucille. Well, you surely have patience, Edith.

Edith. And it's a good thing that I do, or Ted would have made a nervous wreck of me long ago.

(*Boys troop in left. Their costumes have suffered in the chase.*)

Lucille. Look at the ladies. They're all disheveled. What would Auntie Estabrook say?

Ted (*intent*). Where did you find the ice-cream?

Edith. Oh, you'd never guess, of course.—I took it away from three or four thugs, and left them all lying dead in the street.

Ted. Why—why—Edith, that's not true.

THE ESTABROOK NIECES

EDITH. It must be, Ted, because that's what Barbara heard you say.

TED. Barbara?

BARBARA. Yes. You at that window, talking to Sam; I in this chair.

SAM. Wow.

TED. I'm licked. I give up.

DUD. Aha, the master mind meets defeat for once.

CHARLEY. But I don't understand.

SAM. To-morrow, Charley, to-morrow, all shall be made clear to you.

EDITH. Ted, you rascal, what do you mean by all these tricks to-night?

TED. Sister, I knew we wouldn't fool you very long, you're too smart, but ——

EDITH. Flattery. That's old; that won't get you anywhere.

TED. But I thought that all this would keep your party enlivened and make things interesting, even up to the last minute.

MARY. It's certainly done that.

TED. We've worked pretty hard to-night, trying to entertain you girls.

SAM. Yes, and I certainly did my share.

LUCILLE. You did more than your share, Sam. And it was surely entertaining.

TED. Haven't you all enjoyed it?

BARBARA. It's been a very interesting party

LUCILLE. Yes, and quite the most exciting affair I ever attended.

TED. Then if we have made things interesting, why should I be scolded for it?

Dud. That's it exactly.

Barbara. Well, eh—I don't know.

Lucille. You do make a good case for yourselves.

Edith. You see, girls, how he always drags himself out of it. (*Sternly.*) Ted, we don't believe a word you are saying, but I will forgive you on one condition.

Ted. Name it, sister.

Edith. That you will—dish the ice-cream at once.

Ted. Gladly.

(*As* Ted *opens the freezer and the others draw around him, the curtain falls.*)

NOTE TO THE
BOYS AND GIRLS WHO ACT
THE PLAYS

NOTE TO THE BOYS AND GIRLS WHO ACT THE PLAYS

Any group of energetic boys and girls who want to produce plays will be able to do so with success, and with much pleasure and profit to themselves, if they plan their enterprise carefully and work diligently for its accomplishment.

The first and most important task is to obtain a stage manager, or coach. Young people should select someone as a coach who is older and more experienced, and therefore can command their confidence and respect. In addition to a knowledge of the methods of play production, the stage manager must possess the tact, patience, and firmness which will enable him to lead others, and to control the actions of an entire group.

Authority in all things must be given to the stage manager. He must be obeyed without question if the work is to be accomplished. If more than one person attempts to assume control, contradictions, deadlocks, and failure may result. Successful group enterprises in dramatics are impossible without definitely centralized leadership. This does not mean, however, that when the leader is chosen, the members of the group are released from responsibility. Boys and girls who invite an older person to coach them in a play must be alert to do the little things for themselves, so that the stage manager will not be forced to carry the entire load. Above all, his

NOTE TO THE ACTORS

directions must be carried out promptly and thoroughly. The greatest service can be secured from the stage manager only by giving him prompt obedience and faithful support.

The cast should be selected by a small executive committee, working under the guidance of the coach. It is advisable to conduct tryouts by allowing the candidates for parts to read aloud in the auditorium where the play is to be produced. An outline analysis card like the following may prove useful to the judging committee in estimating the comparative merit of the applicants and in avoiding biased or hasty judgments.

A. MANNER ON STAGE:
   Easy or embarrassed; animated or dull?
B. VOICE:
   Strong or weak; pleasing or unpleasant; modulated or monotonous; clear or muffled?
C. FACIAL EXPRESSION:
   Attractive or unattractive; significant or inexpressive?
D. BODILY MOVEMENT:
   Graceful or awkward; virile or ineffectual; concise or vague?
E. SUITABILITY:
   Do the personal characteristics of the candidate fit him for the part? Is the candidate adapted to the rest of the cast by contrast or conformity in height, complexion, voice, manner, or appearance?

In making the selections, the judges should bear in mind that personality and character of the players enter largely into the success of play production. It will be found helpful to select those persons whose cheerfulness, energy, dependability, and unselfishness are outstanding.

As soon as the members of the cast are chosen, the other members of the group, who have not been selected for the cast, should be assigned to the remaining work involved in play production. These duties are just as important as any other and without them the production would be impossible. Many boys and girls find it extremely fascinating to do their share " behind the scenes," helping to make the wheels go around.

The various tasks should be very definitely assigned to certain people, so that they may be accomplished on time. It is best to make and follow an outline of organization, of which the following is an example:

ORGANIZATION—DIVISIONS AND RESPONSIBILITIES:

A.   *The Stage Manager*—He is director of the entire production. His particular duty is to conduct rehearsals, but it is his general privilege to suggest ways and means of carrying out the work in all of its divisions.

B.   *The Executive Committee*—This committee should be chosen first. After selecting the cast and organizing the remaining committees, it coördinates the work of carrying out the plans of the stage manager. Its members assist at all rehearsals, by prompting.

C.   *The Cast*—The players should be responsible for nothing except their parts in the play.

NOTE TO THE ACTORS

D. *Costumes and Properties Committee*—Its members should secure and care for all costumes worn, and all properties actually handled by the players in the course of the play. Properties should be available for use at the first rehearsals, and costumes should be secured at once and made ready for the stage manager's call for dress rehearsals.

E. *Staging and Lighting Committee*—This committee should prepare the scenery, furnish the stage, arrange the lights, and manipulate the curtains. The entrances and exits, and the essential pieces of stage furniture should be in place from the first rehearsals. Full lighting effects should be ready for dress rehearsals.

F. *Business Committee* — This group should undertake advertising and publicity, which must not be delayed if it is to be effective. It should also manage the sale of tickets, the seating of the audiences, and the payment of all bills incurred. No other committee should make an expenditure not authorized by the business committee and the executive committee.

Every member of the group, whether his responsibility is large or small, whether his services are conspicuous or inconspicuous, must remember that to a certain extent all depends on him. A play production is the assembled result of a number of little things done well, and it requires as much team work as an athletic victory. Promptness is essential. Every committee should strive to have its work done not just on time, but ahead of time. Spare time becomes a rare and valuable commodity as the production date draws near.

NOTE TO THE ACTORS

The most detailed and extensive work usually lies with the cast. They will accomplish greater results if they enter their work thoughtfully and follow a definite procedure in it.

First attention should be given to a study of the play as a whole. It is best to have the cast meet together and read parts aloud through the play several times, until they have become quite familiar with the characters and the plot. Then they should look for the element of progression in the play. They will find a number of situations, each growing out of a former situation as a direct result, and all constituting the action of the play, leading to a finality or conclusion. Members of the cast should be very sure to understand each situation in its relation to the whole play, and the operation of cause and effect in the whole. Discussions on such questions as " Why was it necessary for this character to do this? ", " What made him do that? ", " Would it be possible to omit this incident? " will prove helpful in giving insight into the problems of the play.

Boys and girls who are just beginning their experience in acting plays must keep in mind that they are assisting the author to tell the story. The written drama tells only what the characters say. It is the work of the actor to tell how the characters feel, and this he does by expression in speech and action.

After the cast as a whole has agreed on the interpretation to be given the play, each player must undertake a more thorough and minute study of the character he is to represent, always keeping in mind the relation of that character to the other characters and to the development of the plot. Every line and every bit of action should be thought over in an effort to imagine how the part can be made vividly characteristic, and to devise the most effective manner of speaking those lines and carrying out that action. Each player should come to the rehearsals with a fairly definite conception of the manner in which he expects to play his part. Individual conferences with the coach will often prove helpful in this preparation.

As the rehearsing proceeds, the players will find it necessary to make adjustments to one another, each one " tuning in " to the composite result. No character should stand out in distinct contrast to the picture as a whole. A unity of impression, which should be the purpose, can be effected only through he most thoughtful coöperation. Just as numberless rays of light, in passing through a burning lens, are deflected at various angles and focused on one spot, so the attention of the many spectators in the audience must be focused, by everything they see on the stage, to one central point of attention. This point should not remain static; it changes from place to place and from player to player; but there should never be more than one point of attention at one time. It is often the player's duty to make the audience notice someone else. This can be accomplished by remaining quiet while the one who should have attention is playing his part, by looking at the speaker and appearing to listen to him, and by showing the effect of his speech in responsive expression and action.

Attention from the audience will be the best if

NOTE TO THE ACTORS

the players remember that "audience" means an assembly of hearers. The first duty of the actor is to make the audience hear, by means of clear enunciation and adequate tone. It is necessary to speak somewhat more slowly from the stage than in ordinary conversation. A full vocal tone should be produced by breathing deeply and opening the mouth wide in speaking. Avoid speaking while facing the rear of the stage, because it is difficult to make sound carry clearly from such a position.

Lines should never be spoken against continued laughter or confusion in the audience. If a burst of laughter occurs, let everyone on the stage stiffen into a tableau for a single moment, until the audience has been allowed its brief expression. Then, just as soon as a lull occurs, let the character whose speech follows begin that speech, with assurance and positiveness, if possible making a decisive gesture or movement before speaking, and if necessary using a slightly raised tone of voice for the first two or three words.

Unnecessary movements on the stage should be avoided, because they diffuse attention. All movements and gestures should be full of meaning. There should be no more than is necessary for creating the atmosphere and carrying out the action of the play. Have a reason for every step and gesture. From the first, in rehearsing the play, the actors should maintain their exact positions on the stage, as fixed by the stage manager. Movements necessary in the course of the action should be executed so that a pleasing stage picture will always be maintained. Avoid the bunching of characters in one part of the

NOTE TO THE ACTORS

stage. Seek symmetry and balance in arrangement. Keep characters in comparative isolation for those moments when they demand attention. Much can be learned from the motion pictures by observing how, in scenes employing hundreds of people, the chief characters keep in the focus of attention by taking isolated and commanding positions.

In all their efforts, young players must learn to play the game. Keep the interests of the group foremost and forget yourself in your desire and effort to do your part well for the sake of the whole. The best thing boys and girls can gain from amateur dramatics is the spirit of unselfish coöperation—"All for one and one for all."